MY WAR
WITH THE
UNITED STATES

Ludwig Bemelmans

My War with the United States

Illustrated by the Author

The Viking Press

New York

1937

Contents

MY WAR
WITH THE
UNITED STATES

Foreword

IN December 1914 I was sixteen years old and came to America.

The quality of my mind and its information at that time was such that, on sailing for America from the port of Rotterdam, I bought two pistols and much ammunition. With these I intended to protect myself against and fight the Indians.

I had read of them in the books of Karl May and Fenimore Cooper, and intently hoped for their presence without number on the outskirts of New York City.

My second Idea was that the elevated railroad of New York ran over the housetops, adapting itself to the height of the buildings in the manner of a roller coaster.

These Ideas were the consequence of a very alone growing-up in the small villages of Tirol and on the lakes of Upper Austria. The last three years before coming to the United States were spent in a German boarding school.

The Captain of the steamer *Ryndam* persuaded me to return the guns. The shopkeeper in Rotterdam, however, would only exchange them for other hardware, and I traded them for twelve pairs of finely chiseled Solingen scissors and three complicated pocketknives.

On this steamer, the S.S. *Ryndam* of the Holland America Line, was a smoking room. The benches and restful chairs in this saloon were upholstered with very durable, gun-colored material with much horsehair in it.

My plan at the time was to have one strong suit made of this material. I reasoned that such a garment would last me for ten years, and in this time I could put by enough money to go back to Tirol and buy a sawmill which stands in a pine forest on top of a mountain in the Dolomites.

The chapters of this book were translated from the pages of my German Diary which I kept during my service in the United States Army.

The GUARDHOUSE
FORT ONTARIO

Please Don't Shoot

OSWEGO is on Lake Ontario; it is a small town without tall buildings. There is one hotel, the Pontiac, a streetcar, also a theater, in which the Paulist Choristers sang yesterday. The town is very friendly, the air is strong and clear. We are stationed out at Fort Ontario. The grounds of this fortress are spacious; there is an immense parade ground.

The Field Hospital, Unit N, to which I belong, was recruited in New York. The men are all volunteer soldiers and the Officers, doctors. The men are mostly college students or graduates, not ordinary privates. Some of them are older, and professional men; for example, the one who has his bed next to mine in the barracks is a Professor of French at one of the large universities—it is either Harvard or Yale, I believe. His name is Beardsley.

I am very glad of his friendship; he seems to take the whole

11

business we are engaged in as if it did not concern him, as a vacation, never has a serious thought. He takes a peculiar pride in having a very ill-fitting uniform and hat. These military hats are badly enough designed as they are, but he fixes his own so that the rim turns up off his face, which makes him look very inefficient; also he shaves only when he has to. Mostly he sits on his bed and eats a peculiar kind of small white nuts and crosses his legs.

All this is so fine because he is a man of great culture, and I like him so much because I have to think how unbearable a German Professor would be here next to me. In the evening Beardsley looks like a Mexican bandit. He makes no effort to be assigned to better jobs, to win a promotion—he could even have a commission for the asking. But he is happy, and most so when we push a wagon with bread from the bakery back to the barracks every evening; then he sings and says that this is the best time he has ever had, that he is completely happy. Perhaps he has been in some terrible life and now feels happy because he is away from that. He tells me that Schopenhauer states with authority that Happiness is the absence of Unhappiness, which is so obvious and foolish that a backward child could make this observation, but he says I must think about it. I looked this up and it is right; only Schopenhauer says the absence of *"Schmerz,"* which is pain, and in German the word pain covers more than just pain—it means sorrow, trouble, unhappiness. And so Professor Beardsley is perhaps right.

They allowed me to bring my dog along. The Major said to the Adjutant back in New York City: "Say, Charlie, he has a dog, can we use a dog?"

The Adjutant asked: "What kind of a dog is it?"

I said: "A police dog."

Then he leaned back and said to the Major: "It's all right with me."

"All right, son, bring your police dog," said the Major. "What's his name?"

I am glad of this, yet I have never seen anything like it. I cannot think of a German Major calling his Adjutant Charlie and asking him about the dog—and all this time the Major sat in a chair and told me to sit down, and the Adjutant had his legs on the Major's desk. The Major smoked a cigar and smiled and then talked to me in German about beer and food; he also said how much he enjoyed a trip down the Rhine.

We drill here all day long, and workingmen are building new barracks and fixing the old ones up. There is a Colonel here from the regular army, a smart-looking old gentleman with white hair and a trim, well-kept body; he wears boots and spurs and behaves like an Officer. The men tell me that these are West Pointers and that you can always tell them, no matter how old they are.

We are being instructed how to take care of the sick, how to transport men on stretchers, first aid, and how to help in a Hospital.

In our free time we go to motion pictures and entertainments for the soldiers. One is as dull as the other. On Sundays we·go to churches, and afterwards people ask us to their houses for dinner. In all these houses is a soft warm feeling, a desire to be good to us, and the food is simple, good, and plentiful. We also take walks together, and Beardsley has pointed out a piece of scenery which he named "Beautiful Dreck." It was a bitter landscape composed of railroad tracks, signal masts, coal sheds, a factory building and some freight cars, a gas tank, and in the background some manufacturing plant, black with soot. Some of the windows of this building were lit by a vivid gray-blue light and yellow flames shot out of several chimneys. "That is," he said, "beautiful Dreck, and we have lots of it in America."

Dreck is a German word for filth and dirt but it also means manure, mud, dirty fingers. It is a large, able word, *patois,* almost bad; it covers all that was before us, and thereby can be seen that Professor Beardsley knows much. He told me St. Louis had a particularly good portion of "Beautiful Dreck," but that the best he knew could be seen in the Jersey Meadows, where it covers almost a whole countryside.

One day the Wardmaster of Ward Number Three swam too far out into Lake Ontario and drowned, and I became the Wardmaster. This ward was filled with oldtime soldiers; they call themselves "Oldtimers" and had recently been with Mr. Pershing in Mexico. They were distinguished from all other soldiers in that they had overcoats and uniforms of what they called the "Old Issue," a cloth of much better quality than the new and also of better color, and they were very proud of khaki uniforms that were almost white from much wear and bleaching. These uniforms of course they did not wear; they hung in their closets. They were middle-aged men, and those in our ward suffered from some amorous diseases which they mentioned with pride, considering those who did not have either the disease or the memory of it not quite complete soldiers. Among my duties was to give them their medicines, to take pulse, temperature, and respiration, and the difficult job of turning the lights out at nine o'clock. They read, played cards, talked, and did not want to go to sleep. All objects they used had to be sterilized; I had to wear rubber gloves most of the time.

The first few nights after I took charge I said: "Lights out" when it was nine, turned the lights out, and went to the room outside, where I wrote out reports. But I could see that they turned the lights on again as soon as I was out of the room. This worried me a great deal, because "Lights out" means "Lights out" and there must be discipline in an army. I could not understand that these men who were "Oldtimers" did not understand that in Germany this would have been unthinkable. The third night I intended to do something about it. I walked into the room and waited until it was nine, then I turned out the light but did not go out. One of the men next to the light said: "Hey, buddy, turn on that light, like a good boy."

I told him that I was not "a good boy," but the Wardmaster in charge, and that the orders were to turn the lights out.

"That's right," said the Oldtimer, "but it doesn't say that you can't turn them on again!"

Then another shouted: "Turn on that light, Heinie"; then one of them came in his pajamas and turned on the light, pushing me against the wall, and they all laughed. When he was back in bed, I turned the light out again, and at that moment every one of them threw something at me, even two glass ducks, which is the name for the watering bottles.

I ran over to the barracks and got my Colt forty-five, strapped it around myself, and then I came back in the room with the gun in my hand. I told them that I would turn the lights out again and the first man who would come near me, get out of bed, or even make a noise, would be shot. I turned out the lights again—it was about ten o'clock. They howled with joy, threw all the rest of the things they had not thrown before, and I shot twice into the room over their heads. As yet I did not want to hurt any of them, but I would have shot the first man who came near me.

There was silence after this and then people came running, nurses, orderlies, patients from the other wards, and the Officer of the Day. He took my gun away from me and told me to consider myself under arrest and go to my barracks. The next day at ten o'clock an orderly told me to come to headquarters and see the Colonel.

Most of the Officers were in his room. I saluted in correct military fashion according to their rank, first the Colonel, then the Major, the Captain after, and lastly two First Lieutenants, each with a click of the heels and a slight bow from the waist, which was both elegant and correct and as I had seen the German Officers do.

The Colonel sat behind a desk; he was the very little man who always made speeches about an irrigation project in some country with malaria which he had been responsible for—I think it was Manila, but we heard this speech so often that I have forgotten just where it was.

He started to say, looking out of the window: "The basic function of a Hospital, Private Bemelmans, is to cure men, not to shoot them."

Then he turned around and laughed, and asked me to tell them how it happened. They laughed loud when I told them and said that after all I had done the right thing, in intention that is; they agreed that discipline is the first requisite of an Army, and when I informed them that either one had to enforce it or leave it alone and let the patients run the hospital, they nodded and laughed some more, and the Colonel said that

he thought I would do more good to the service if I were outside the Hospital on the guard, since obviously I was a military
man and not suited to ward duty. My gun was on his desk all
this time. He gave it back to me and said: "But please don't
shoot," and then he said that he would take care that I was
transferred to the guard.

From then on, he, the Colonel, and all the Officers smile
when they see me and it makes me mad.

But apparently there is no room for me on the guard as yet,
and Beardsley and I have no particular assignment except to
drill with Captain Pedley. He is a fine man, he has a likeness
to President Wilson on account of his teeth, and while he is
not a military man, he is not altogether so foolish and ama-
teurish as most of the others are when they drill us—particularly the fat Officers who are squeezed into creaky leather
puttees, get out of breath, and are unable to get us back into
formation once they have given two or three commands. The
regular army sergeant has to help them or they dismiss us and
make us fall into our "original places." Also they lack that
distance which must be in an army, because at rest they talk to
the men about all kinds of things, even the movies; and one of
them even lay down in the grass with us and picked his teeth
while he told us about how he bought a house in Flushing and
all the woodwork was painted, and when he had some of it
scraped off there was some genuine kind of wood under the
paint that is very valuable, and how mad it made him that the
former owner was so stupid to cover it up and now he had to
have all the wood scraped, it cost a lot of money.

Of course all the men are from colleges or as good as he is,
but then they are privates now and he is an Officer. He also
spoke to me at that time in German—"*Wie geht es Ihnen?*" he

said and a few sentences like that—and he tells us that he has been in Heidelberg and Vienna and that the post-graduate courses in Vienna are a fake, but very fine for drinking and girls. Afterwards we drill again. This seems wrong to me.

None of these Officers can ride, fence, or fight; most of them wear glasses. Only the Colonel is a West Pointer, but he is very old and continually makes speeches, mostly in Oswego, on that irrigation project.

We have a Glee Club and there are dances. Beardsley and I do not go out much; but there is one from New York, a very tall man, in fact the tallest of all the men, who takes leaves over the weekend and says he goes to New York. He keeps to himself, has a silver hairbrush, and says he is in Society. He is an architect; but Beardsley, who knows New York and Society, says that he is not in the Register, but that he thinks he has seen him at some parties where everyone can get in.

Beardsley has found a fine way to fool the Officers. At inspection, they look at the bed to see if the linen is clean. We have to wash it ourselves and that is a lot of unpleasant work, so he has told me how one keeps one sheet clean by putting it in paper and carefully away. On Saturday, then, we take the usual sheets and the pillowcase off and we take the clean sheet out of the paper and fold it so that a quarter of it covers the top of the mattress. Then it is turned back, comes up over the blanket as if it were the second sheet, and then the end is tucked in around the pillow and the bed looks snow-white and passes. After inspection the white sheet is carefully folded up again and put back into the locker for next Saturday and the old sheets are used during the week.

We are now on the roster for Kitchen Police and this is a miserable job, particularly as the cook—his name is Lichten—burns the beans to the bottom of two square tin tubs which are as deep as an ashcan. When we have washed them we have to go with head and shoulders to the bottom of these receptacles and with a teaspoon scrape the black crust from the bottom. The water is greasy and not hot and it is a filthy job.

The nurses that came up from New York are not what we thought they would be. The one at the head of them is a crude person with a revolting fat body and the face of a streetcar conductor; she also has a stupid walk and a common voice. She teaches us how to make beds, take temperatures, and change the linen of patients in bed without moving them. All the men detest to be taught this by women and much more so when she does it; they are very clumsy at it and cannot make the neat corners that seem so simple to women. But because they know this, they make us feel silly. There is only one . . . she is young and lithe and has lovely black hair.

On Sunday afternoon they all sit down at the edge of the parade ground and look out over Lake Ontario; from far away they look like gulls at rest in their white dresses. I want to show them that we can do some things that they can't do and also impress the little nurse, and I have arranged to get a horse from the livery stable. Down close to where they sit is a wide ditch and I will ride up, gallop, and jump that ditch. The horse I got is seemingly good enough to do that. I rode along, then let him out when he came to the ditch. He stopped so suddenly that I was thrown over his head, taking the bridle with me; it came off and the horse ran back, jumping over two of the Major's children who were playing in front of Officers' Row.

Then he ran down to where our mules eat grass and a quarter-master helped me get him. Next day there is a note on the bulletin board, saying: "Privates will not ride in front of Officers' Row," and it is signed by the Colonel.

the Kitchen of the Isolation Hospital.

FORT ONTARIO.

The Operation

WE have two scarlet fever cases, and a sign is stuck on the bulletin board, that two men are wanted to take care of them, two men who have had scarlet fever and therefore are immune to it. Beardsley and I volunteer for this job; we both have had this fever.

The Isolation Hospital, a little brick building that has been given this title, is far away from all other houses. It has two small rooms for the patients, one for each, and a room for Beardsley and me, besides a bathroom, a combination kitchen and living room, and a porch. There is a telephone, and the

21

house is stocked with linen, medicaments, hospital supplies, and dishes.

The patients are there already. One is a quiet, colorless man; the other, named Carey, is a mean, quarrelsome lout, without manners and stupid. We are to stay there, one on night duty, the other on day, never leave the building, and take care of the patients.

The house stands on a hill, on one side the old fortress, in front of it the lake, in back the parade ground; and anyone coming can be seen long before he arrives. You have to cross the wide field on a narrow path. Along this path our food is brought, and after half an hour's exposure to cold and wind it is stale and not very good even if warmed up. The patients get milk and Zwieback. It is cold, and we have to keep a fire going all day long. Carey is in the little room at the right; on the left is the other man.

After the men had run through half the length of their sickness, the Doctor, who is a Captain named Grillmeyer, told us that now they could have food, that they must be built up with eggs, meat, vegetables. It is very fortunate that Beardsley can cook, and Captain Grillmeyer leaves us an order for the main kitchen and the commissary to supply whatever we need for the patients.

The big Hospital is filled; there are many patients, and Captain Grillmeyer is more a surgeon than a physician. He is busy operating all day and he will not come for a while, but will call up every evening, and if anything should happen we are to get in touch with him immediately.

We can order eggs, steaks, chops, vegetables, rice, noodles, sugar, flour, and many more things, even dried fruit and chocolate. In that foolish language which Beardsley and I talk, concocted of distorted words, elaborate gestures, Oh's and Ah's, the raising of eyebrows, and deep nods, we decide after the patients are asleep that we are more hungry than they and need building up ourselves, and that they can be kept without harm on a liquid diet for another week or so.

Beardsley is a fine cook. Many of the seasonings that he needs are missing, but he does well with what he has. The groceries and meats arrive promptly when ordered, the baskets are left on our porch, and we stand around the oven and fry and broil and stew ourselves into a contented after-dinner state twice every day, and have besides thick ham and eggs for breakfast. No wine, but cigars—Beardsley bought a box of them before we came.

Carey is troublesome; he smells the good food and all day long he wants to get up, so we have to chase him back to bed. Also we have read all the magazines and books that are here and talked ourselves out of everything we know that is inter-esting. This is a dull, dead, rainy Saturday night. We don't know what to do with ourselves; our patient is unbearably stupid. . . . But Beardsley gets a magnificent Idea.

Beardsley went into Carey's room and looked at him with suspicion, felt his head, and asked him to show his tongue.

A while after he sent me in to look at him; I had to feel his abdomen and shake my head.

Later we both went in and looked at him and then at each other and walked out again.

The door was left open so that Carey could hear us and, after we had eaten our—or rather his—custard, Beardsley said to me: "I have seen it happen again and again; just when you think they're out of it, this terrible complication sets in. God,

I hope this poor devil hasn't got it! Should we call Grill-meyer?" he asked himself and then answered: "Not yet." He went in to look at Carey again.

Carey sat at the head of his bed, on the pillows, clamped to the iron bars and ready to kick with his feet; but Beardsley calmed him with oily words and then he allowed us to pull up the top of his pajamas and feel his abdomen. He was white, his shapeless mouth open, and he breathed heavily.

We went back to our cigars and Beardsley told me a loud story of one man, such a one as this poor boy Carey, a case so identical that the patient looked exactly like him, with precisely the same symptoms and even color of eyes. The Doctor came too late; he was dead in two hours—died in horrible pain—his spine contracted to such a degree that his head was bent back between his legs; he was like a ring with the navel on the outside—blue with green spots all over. They had to bury him in a round coffin.

"But we're not going to take a chance like that with Carey," said Beardsley—and then in a low voice, as if he was afraid the patient could hear and be upset, he added, pointing at himself: "Not I, I'm responsible for this man. Close the door; I'm calling Captain Grillmeyer on the phone, this minute."

I closed the door and we heard the bedsprings creak as Carey climbed out of bed to listen at the door.

Beardsley came back from the phone and told me that Grill-meyer was standing by, that Carey had the unmistakable signs of the dread disease, and that he, Grillmeyer, thought it best to operate. The room to work in, Operating Room Number One, would be kept free, a wagon sent over, and all this would take place in about half an hour.

We gave Carey enough time to get back into bed and opened

the door. Beardsley asked him if he had any relatives and where they lived.

I put my hand on his head and Beardsley looked at him and said: "Steady, Carey, you'll be allright, just relax."

We brought him a pad of paper and a pencil, also an envelope with a stamp, turned out the big light, adjusted his pillow, put a white screen around his bed, and left him to go and drink more coffee and finish the cigars.

He was quiet. When he saw us, he looked down; he had not written anything but chewed on the pencil. He was almost green. I took his temperature again and his pulse, and asked him to say: "Ahh." Beardsley pressed his stomach so hard that he yelled. "Aha!" said Beardsley.

Then we made him use a bottle for Analysis and Beardsley came back with the result, in a small test tube. It was black coffee, but Carey gave only one quick look. Beardsley held it up to the light and said: "We might as well tell him now, this is the proof!"

For such an Operation, explained Beardsley, the entire cover of the stomach is removed, not with one incision but with four. He demonstrated this on his own person: two cuts ran from where the legs meet, left and right to the hips; the other two from there up to the neck. The entire covering of the abdomen is lifted off and with it also that which makes a man most proud of himself and which is no good after being replaced.

Beardsley went out, tied Doctor Grillmeyer's white gown around himself, stuffed cotton in his nose, and put on operating gloves. We washed Carey's stomach with soap and water and then shaved it and painted the area where the incisions would run with Iodine; then we gave him an enema.

It was too much; Carey turned gray and blue with almost

the green spots of the dread disease on him. His eyelids fluttered like the wings of a young butterfly and the pupils almost disappeared under the upper lids. At this moment the telephone rang and Grillmeyer called for his daily report. He also announced that he would be over tomorrow.

It was good for us at this moment that Carey was so without mind. When he came to, we informed him that sometimes in rare cases the crisis passes without need of the knife and that he looked like one of these fortunates. If he felt no pain for the next hour, he would be safe.

We both sat on his bed with watch in hand for the next hour. There was no sign of pain; he continually assured us how good he felt. He was enthusiastic about his condition even when Doctor Grillmeyer came the next day. We gave him a cigar for lunch.

Summer Sprouts

WE are going to produce an Entertainment at the Hotel
Pontiac in Oswego. Private Pierre Loving is making the ar-
rangements for it, the Society architect is also busy with it.
Tickets will be sold; the beau monde of Oswego will be there,
and the Officers and their wives; there will be dancing after
the theater. The entertainment itself consists of two parts: the
first is a play, *A Night at an Inn* by Lord Dunsany, followed
by *Fauns' Rout*. I am to appear in this as faun; it is a pantomime, luckily I have little to do. I am painted dark brown all

27

over and come out from behind a tree, then I dance a short while and during most of the action I sit on the side of the stage and play on my reeds. Beardsley laughs and I am not very happy at the whole business, particularly not since one of our soldiers has told me that I have a lovely body. He wants to help me paint it.

I will ask Evelyn to this party. She can bring her mother, watch the show, and afterwards we will dance.

I have known Evelyn for a month. She goes to Normal School in Oswego; I met her at a church party. On Sundays she comes out to the Fort and we walk around and sit on the lawn above the Fortress, under the flag in the shelter of a rock. The wind here is so strong that the flag up on the pole continually makes a fluttering noise—pupupupupupup—almost like a small motorboat. We look out over the lake.

One time I asked her to come earlier than usual and when she did not appear, I asked some of the men if they had not seen her. She has lovely white skin, red hair, and freckles which in Germany we call "Summer sprouts," so I asked the men if they had seen the girl with the Summer sprouts. Since then they call her "Summer sprouts." I have asked them not to, but they say it loud in the city—"Hello, Summer sprouts." She does not like this at all, but I can do nothing about it. She is very proper, and when I try to put my arm around her soft body, she wiggles loose, holds both my hands, and says: "Look at the lake."

Some days in the evening, when I am not going anywhere with Beardsley, I come to her house and the Family are very nice. They even leave us alone on the porch, but she only straightens out her dress and says: "Please don't." But they have my picture in an album on the table and under it is written: "Our soldier boy."

After she says "Don't," she arranges her hair and closes her mouth in a thin line with the lips almost swallowed. Her eyes are straight ahead as if she saw something, and she sits up stiff and straight. Beardsley tells me to ignore the "Don't"; he says it is part of a nice girl's routine, but when I ignored it, she slapped me harder than the game would seem to call for and called me a cad. Beardsley tells me that a "cad" is not very bad, to ignore the "cad" also. But I have had enough and we leave it as is and just sit quietly.

Evelyn loves to go with me to the New York Candy Kitchen, the most elegant icecream parlor in Oswego, where all the other girls she knows go with their fellows. None of them are soldiers. We always sit close to them and Evelyn converses in French with me loud enough so they can all hear it. When we walk out, everybody is quiet and looks after us, and at the door she turns and says something like: *"Ah—c'est dommage!"* She loves this word and uses it continually without need. Outside she speaks English again.

On the night of the entertainment, I came down early and looked for her. She sat in the second row with her mother to the left of her. I could see them through the opening between curtain and stage. Evelyn had on a lovely white dress of many layers of gauze, and out of her dress shone her red hair, her green eyes, and the lovely lines of her neck and shoulders.

The play earned great applause. For *Fauns' Rout,* I put on the brown paint and wear a thin strap around my middle with artificial leaves pinned on to it. When I finished dancing and sat down, I saw that a soldier who is not my friend was sitting next to Summer sprouts, very close to her; also he talked to her behind the program.

This man is related to some political boss in Pennsylvania and has gotten away with much already; also he has a room in Oswego and a car. I am afraid my evening will be ruined if I do not get out there very quickly.

After the curtain went down I ran to the dressing rooms that are below the stage and, because I was in a great hurry, I cleaned only my face and my hands to the wristbones; the rest I left brown and over it put on my shirt and Uniform and then ran up.

Evelyn sat with the soldier, but he got up and said a few nice words to me, to which I had no answer because I was too mad. He left to dance with another girl, also beautiful.

It became a lovely evening. The little Colonel was there and he was very pleasant; he did not make a speech. We had supper and punch that somebody had donated, the dancing started, and there was in this room a happiness that should always be, but seldom is, at such assemblies.

Among the dances was one called John Paul Jones and others where the ladies ran across the floor and chose their partners. Evelyn ran to me, I ran to her when this game was played the other way, and we danced more and faster and held each other tightly. Her cheeks were red with excitement, and the little hairs on the nape of her neck were lovelier than anything I have ever seen, also her ears. I looked at all this closely while we danced.

The orchestra played very fast pieces and it got very warm; we danced every dance. I had forgotten completely about my paint, and I think that this paint was not very good—with the heat and sweating it began to come off. It ran down my wet body to the elbows, to the wrists, and into the palms of the hand, from there to the fingers, and dripped down to the new white dress of my Evelyn. I had marked the white satin bodice of the dress with black fingers and palms all over. I think I could have kissed her often that night, but her mother told her about the dress, the soldiers stopped and laughed and said: "Look at Summer sprouts," and that was the end. She went home.

Entrance to the Old Fort, Ontario

The Good Prisoners

THE Guardhouse at Fort Ontario is next to a long dipping road that runs into the Fort from an underpass, over which goes a railroad. The tunnel is long and of heavy stone construction. I am now on guard there; there is a strange way to do this. When someone approaches the Fort out of the tunnel, I wait until he is close enough, then I shout:

"Halt, who goes there?"

The halted one answers: "Friend."

Then I shout: "Advance, Friend, to be recognized," and the Friend advances.

This seems childish to me, as an enemy would hardly announce himself, but perhaps it is some form carried over from the Indian wars or something I do not understand.

I always have trouble in shouting the word "recognized." Most of the Officers laugh, and one night a new Major from Washington who did not know about this came into the Fort

33

and when I stopped him he said: "My God! Are the Germans this far?" Then he laughed and said in that peculiar way Americans speak German, with the mouth too hollow and in back of the teeth:

"Wie geht es Ihnen, mein Herr?"

Since then all the Officers laugh, also the guards; they come out to see me do this and say: "Come on, Bemmy, go get him, do your stuff," and then roar with amusement, as if I were a comedian giving a performance, and they all imitate my "recognized."

We also have a duty that is called "Chase Prisoners"—walking six feet behind them. They wear stiff fatigue clothes of heavy blue canvas much too big for them, on the back of their coats a large P which means "Prisoner." They are not allowed to salute the Officers, which is no punishment, but we the guards must salute.

We have different places to chase them—to clean windows in the Officers' houses, shovel coal, deliver coal, collect garbage, collect ashes, cut grass, and many such kinds of work. They are not, of course, criminals or prisoners of war; they are soldiers who stay out late, get drunk, argue with officers, and their worst offense seems to be one called A.W.O.L.—which means absent without official leave.

Two of the prisoners, the nicest, are men who deserted the Army to join the Navy, or the other way round, and they are here for four months for this offense. They are my prisoners and we get along very well. They sing most of the time and make jokes, many of them funny, mostly when we work in Officers' houses.

The circumstances of Army Officers here—or for that matter in any other post—seem to me not overly desirable, very narrow and dull, and more so when there is no war. The houses are all alike, the wives also, and likewise the children. A poor kind of elegance is in these houses; it is made of white tennis trousers, bridge tables, a few magazines, and a piano. The furniture is bad, the rooms no better than in a house that might belong to a man like Evelyn's father, who is a repair man.

I feel there must be great jealousy among them, especially when one has what the others have not. There is one man here who drives a shiny black packard, which is too long for the carage and sticks out of the back all day. It seems to be an object of trouble. He also has a beautiful wife and better riding boots, and at his house the prisoners and I get cake and pie, which is against regulations.

The orders today are take the prisoners to the old Fortress and have them chop wood. We get two axes and I march them over. I have noticed that among the grass in the old Fort and on the lawns that lead to it, many little flowers grow; they are like our own small field flowers in Tirol. Usually the grass in America seems to me just green, flowerless grass, but here are small white flowers, a little kind of bluebell, buttercups, and also sorrel.

The inside of the Fortress is beautiful America to me; I people it with such of this country's history as I have thought together for myself. It most probably is all wrong, because I hear that the Fort was built against the French, but for me they were Indians and I see them riding around outside shooting flaming arrows.

The prisoners are hot; they have taken off their coats and their hats, which are as foolish as the coats—like sailors' hats only without any shape whatever, or more like a baby's hat, blue, stiff, and would be difficult to draw, but it is necessary to complete the rest of the costume.

The men have chopped much wood, a large pile of it, and it soon will be time to take them back to the Guardhouse. In the past weeks the prisoners and I have become good friends; we talk always, even when I chase them, six feet apart. They talk loud ahead of them, as they cannot turn around, and I answer from the back.

The prisoners both have German parents, and they have German names, also blue eyes, blond hair, and the shapes of their heads are better because they are born here. They know many German words.

There is no one around; the Fort is in a close ring around us; and they ask if they can stop chopping. It's almost time to go back, so I say: "Yes, of course."

The sunshine is warm in here and there is no wind from the lake. We sit down together and rest and talk. They lay back and stretch in the sun and then turn around and eat blades of grass.

One of them asks me if I ever shot my gun off. I say yes and I tell them the Affair in Ward Number Three. They both agree that I did the right thing.

The other one, Walter is his name, says he is a gunsmith and small arms mechanic and that he knows all about automatics. He asks if I know how the gun is put together and taken apart.

I don't know; I have never taken it apart and I tell him this. Then Fred, the other, says: "He'll take it apart for you and show you." Of course I know that this is a complete stupidity and against all orders to give a prisoner your gun; it is to laugh. But I like them so much and have such faith in them that I wish not to offend them, but give them proof of my friendship. Besides, if they wish to make trouble, here are two axes with long handles; and another thing is that they have only three more weeks to serve to be free.

Therefore I give my gun to Walter.

He pulled the magazine out, took the bullets out of it. With expert simplicity he changed the gun into little pieces, springs, bolts, screws; everything lay in his lap. He explained the why of everything, put it together, took it apart once more—it was very interesting—when we heard footsteps from the hall that leads into the Fort.

I took the part I had, which was the handle, and stuck it in the holster. Fred and Walter picked up the bullets, springs, screws, etc., etc., etc., and started quickly to chop wood.

The Officer of the Day was the one that made the steps. He is young, arrogant, and the only one that none of the men and not even his own brother Officers like. He looks much like a movie actor and wears such a kind of mustache with wax at the end of it.

He feels that something is wrong and does not go away. Then the whistles blow; it is noon over in Oswego and time to march the men back, but the Officer comes along, close behind me, and follows us to the Guardhouse. This is not as it should be.

After we got to the Guardhouse I locked the two prisoners in the big cage where all of them are together. The Officer of the Day is still around, but while he looks down to the underpass out of the door, I stand with my back to the cage so he cannot see it if he turns around and hold my hands open in back of me. Fred and Walter put all the missing parts into my hands. I keep them in back of me and walk over to the lavatory. There I lock the door and sit down. I have seen Walter put the gun together, fast and easy as a simple toy, yet I cannot do it. I am hot and nervous; every time I think I have it, it is wrong—the gun falls apart, or the spring jumps out, or I can't get the magazine in.

Therefore I come out again and move over to the cage. I hand the gun back through the bars, standing again with my shoulders against them, because the unpleasant First Lieutenant is still there. I give them the gun parts and all and Walter goes to his own lavatory with it; there he puts it together and gives it back to me.

Now I disappear again, to put it back in the holster, and then I can go into the Guardroom and hang it with my belt, up on a rack, where all the others are.

Uncle's Hotel in KLOBENSTEIN. SÜD-TIROL

Mad Maître d'Hôtel

I HAVE read on the bulletin board that a Hospital for the Insane will be organized in Buffalo, at Fort Porter. They need attendants there and do not wish to force anyone into this work; men are asked to volunteer for it. I am very much interested in this and only regret that Beardsley will not come along. My transfer is arranged and I leave in a few days.

The train from Oswego reached Buffalo at six in the morning and I took a streetcar that was filled with very strong-smelling Italian workingmen out to Fort Porter.

The Fort is not a Fort as one might imagine, such for example as Fort Ontario. It has no moat, ramparts, battlements, or any military appearance at all. It is about half an hour's slow streetcar ride outside of the city of Buffalo and is a collection of army buildings, red and a grayish blue. A long house is the most prominent, in which are two large messhalls and kitchens. A smaller group, the non-commissioned Officers' houses, is on the most windy corner of the large ground and faces toward the river, also with an outlook toward the lake. On the corner between these two stands a square building, the Post Hospital.

Workingmen are busy making the houses over into an emergency Insane Asylum. The windows are heavily barred, the floors covered with a slippery kind of surface. One large room in the basement of the biggest house is made ready to give treatments in bathtubs that have a continuous in-and-out flow of water that is kept at certain temperatures. With these bathtubs go some kind of canvas covers to tie patients down on and in this is the first note of mischief or cruelty.

There is another room down there, a long one with a needle shower at the end that looks like a parrot cage with all the horizontal wires taken off. Away from it at the other end is a small marble table, on it a hose which throws a strong current of almost solid water, so tightly compressed is it. It can be shot at the other end, into the cage, as if from a garden hose.

There is cement mixing, carpentering, and hammering all over the place, and people stand around, as on all places where something is being built, and watch and give advice. So far, except for the bathing establishment, it is no more exciting than the building of any kind of a house.

I took a day off and went to look at Niagara Falls. It is perhaps because I took a streetcar out there that I felt they were about half as big as I thought they would be. The thrilling spot is where the water turns down and I made a shade of my hands and looked only on that, shutting out all the scenery. That was a powerful sensation. I am sorry that the Falls are surrounded by what Beardsley calls "Beautiful Dreck." Very interesting was a story that the conductor of the streetcar that took me back told me about the Falls.

A tug belonging to the Shredded Wheat Company, which makes a breakfast food and has a factory near by, broke its rudder and drifted toward the Falls, helpless. A little away from where the water falls down, the tug got stuck on a rock.

The Police and the Fire Department of Buffalo raced out to help them. This took a long time, and the men on the tug looking down could see and hear how the tug slowly moved inch by inch, scraping over the rock, either to be more firmly grounded, or else to go over and down. The Police came in the dark; they tried to shoot safety lines to the tug, but could not reach it. A heavy fog sat on the waters, and not until the sun rose were they able to shoot the line over to the tug. When they managed to get the men off, all of their hair had turned white from horror in this terrible night.

More soldiers are arriving; they know nothing of an Insane Hospital and also nothing of Insanity.

Today, a new group of men have come to us, Nurses, Attendants, and Doctors, and many more soldiers, also a Catholic Chaplain with a studious, earnest face; he is very young.

Many of the men are male nurses from the State Hospitals for the Insane. I observe them carefully—they are all strong, but I expected some sign of their profession on them, just what I do not know—this is, however, not apparent in them. They seem ordinary, normal, healthy people and talk of what anybody else talks of.

One of them, who seems the most important of the group, is a tall Irishman with a shock of flaming red electric hair that stands in a bush, sideway as if the wind were tilting it, or like the comb of a rooster on one side of his head. He has freckles, even on his fingernails, and a way of holding his head as if he were looking over a mass of people and listening into distance up and on one side, to the side where his hair points. He is immaculate; his arms and legs are like oak timbers, so strong they have a curve in them. There is also red hair on his hands, he holds them open at his side; he talks little, eats very fast, walks around the Hospital all day, and speaks a strong dialect, which of course must be Irish. It is an English with which he takes more air than is normally needed to say anything and, while it is loud, he seems to talk in, instead of out, with his breathing. I like him.

We have had several lessons in Anatomy. For this purpose skeletons have been shown, stereopticon pictures of the inside of the body. I attend these lectures with great interest and make drawings of all I see and read; therefore I soon know the names of all the bones, the most important muscles, and understand the body's construction, its contents, the position of the organs; and when I see people walk, or stand up after such a lesson, the solemn wonder of ourselves fills me with a deep respect. I feel that when I see children run, there is much happiness in understanding a small part of this organism. The

Doctor who gives these lessons is addressing himself almost completely to me alone, as the others are not very excited about it.

The Insane Asylum is finished and the Irishman is really in charge. There are Lady Nurses, regular Army nurses of a dreadful caliber, women who look like what we refer to in Germany as "*Canaille.*" They are gross and not women at all, particularly not in walk and voice.

Among the instructions we are given is this: never to leave the nurses unprotected or alone in a ward with patients. This seems like one of Beardsley's funny ideas; I am sure they could protect themselves and that no man would do them harm. I have never seen such formidable women, with shoes like they wear and legs like our barefooted peasants'.

There are more lessons and they are getting closer to the work. Always lock the door behind yourself when entering or leaving a ward. The most important rule is never, never to bring arms, knives, scissors, razorblades, razors, or any other instrument that might be a weapon into the wards. The patients are to be fed with spoons only.

The first patients arrived today. It was late at night, but many people waited outside on the street for the long train of ambulances and cars that came up from the railroad station with the patients and the guards that have been their attendants.

These men, the ill ones, seem stupefied and tired; some are in straitjackets and have a guard each. They are all taken to the basement where the baths are. I am told that they have been transported from Brest and, except for this evening, have not been out of their clothing. I do not know whether this is true, it seems possible. Their clothes are filthy, they have beards, also there is a sickening stench about them and their underclothing is foul.

They are bathed and then assigned to wards.

The Doctors do this. The red Irishman is in the middle of all this. To every ward there is assigned a regular State Asylum trained attendant and a novice soldier. The patients get milk, pajamas and bathrobes, and slippers that give them no foothold on the polished floors, while we have strong shoes with rubber so we can stand our ground when anything happens.

There are rows of solitary cells with what the Irishman calls "the tough customers" in them. They have what we believe to be mad faces, as bad as those that actors, mediocre ones, make when they are in horror plays. From that row comes howling. Some of these men have besides the mental sickness other vile diseases; it would be best to kill them, says the Irishman, that seems the kindest thing to do.

The night they arrived seemed very crisp with danger and excitement, but nothing happened. They sat on their beds and seemed no different from any other patients; some of them wept and mumbled to themselves.

It is a cruel thing to think, but I was disappointed, as were also all the other new men. We thought they might do some funny things, but the Irishman says to wait, they will, and too much of it, in a little while.

He has a definite, rough, and authoritive way with them; they are absolutely in his charge. He lets them know that by word and gesture and the tone of his voice. His personality seems to have developed out of doing this for years. It is in the way he stands and walks, also in the look in his eyes—they are water-blue and penetrate and are strong.

The patients have been here for a while now. I have learned
to know their faces and many things have happened. They
are not funny, but sadder than anything I thought could be
and never in the least to laugh at. They are heavy, disturbing
cases, mostly locked into their inner selves, their condition to
be seen only in their eyes and also when they stand at the
barred windows and look out into the trees and the street with
free people walking up and down and trying to look in. They
pace, and something of their unhappiness and condition jumps
over to me. The Irishman says one must never feel sorry for
them or understand, or attempt to understand, them and not
to talk to them. But the transfer of their misery makes me limp
and terribly tired.

The patients have small duties to perform—make beds,
sweep, dust, wash windows on the inside. The men in this
ward suffer from an illness which makes them periodically
dangerous. It can be felt coming on; the unrest and disturbance
in their minds gets out of all bounds and beyond their power
to control it. They get irritable all at once and refuse to obey,
grumble at any instruction given them. Then they have to be
watched, and all at once without warning their control breaks,
they jump and attack. In rare cases other patients are the
object, but mostly the wardmaster. They seem to go for the
men from the back and, since they are soldiers and can fight,
it is a great deal of work to overcome them. They are terribly
strong once they have a hold, and in this state they cannot
feel pain. At the least sign of fighting, the Wardmasters from
the other wards come in and help. As many as six men fall
on one patient; they choke him and hold him down until the
man is blue in the face.

The first time I saw a fight I was unable to do anything but try and stand it. It is degrading and miserable, yet one cannot look away. After the patient is overcome, the men carry him down to the continuous bath, where he is left to soak in water in changing temperatures for, I hear, as much as twenty hours. When they come out, they are without any strength and then there is no trouble for several weeks. I have not heard of patients fighting together. This is strange. In almost all cases the others stand by and look; seldom do they help the nurse.

Those who howl in the solitary cells are left there. When the men go in to feed one of them, they rush in like a football team, almost on signal. One opens the door, the others go after the patient, to bring him food or to clean the place.

There are also two religious cases. One has worn the skin from his knees, sliding on them in continuous prayer. A new case has arrived and been put in with him; I went to see him. I have a passkey and have become careless. I locked the door behind me, but the man I came to visit was around the corner of the room where I could not see him. This Hospital is a makeshift building; in a real Insane Hospital there are no corners around which one cannot see. As I walked forward, he jumped at me from the bed and closed his fingers around my throat.

I felt singing in my ears, not much pain. I could not breathe, I saw the religious patient for a while and he swam away into a darkness that was bluish. I felt a bang on my head and nothing more until I came to in another room of the Hospital. It had to be kept quiet because I had no right to go in there. The fortunate thing was that I fell against the door with the patient, and the loud bang brought the Irishman.

At first the attacks on the patients and the way they were

choked into a corner made me hate the Irishman and all the other attendants. But even before the attack on me I already knew it was the only thing that could be done there and then. They are as kind as they can be, but they would be dead if they did not instill fear, and of course they fight only when they absolutely must. Also when the patients get out of the baths, the attendants are as nice to them as they are to anyone.

In this ward are also other interesting cases. There is a glass man. A mattress has to be kept on the floor next to his bed, because he is afraid of falling out and breaking. He moves everywhere with care, he screams when anyone comes too near him and sits down with great apprehension. And there are two men who are like puppets. In the morning they have to be sat up in bed, and they sit motionless. They have to be stood up, and if one were to take their arms in the morning and raise them over their heads, the arms would still be that way at night. Another patient repeats one word, the sound of which he likes, endlessly, over and over in monotone.

The most pitiful of all the men are several cases who suffer from persecution fear. They stuff magazines into their bath-robes and sit in corners; they are certain we wish to kill them, stab or shoot at them. They have to be forcefully fed because they think that all food given them is poison. Or we have to eat a little of it ourselves in front of them or give them the trays of other patients who have already started eating. If they still refuse to eat, we sometimes just leave the food. They do not look at it, or curse and upset it, or smear it on themselves, but when we go out—in most cases it happens the moment we are gone—they ravenously eat everything.

They never sleep; at times they doze off in the middle of the night, but only to rise with horrible shrieks from their beds, and in the night these wards are most unhappy. God have pity on these men or let them die.

Of no use at all is religion or the young Chaplain; he feels that, I think, because he is unhappy himself. It made him mad that one woman who visited her husband here seems to be worried only whether he went to confession before he got insane. Yet I think, with its great promise of miracle and power and its character of mysterium, the Catholic religion would be the one most easy to help these patients; the transfer from their own make-believe horror to the church would be easier. I cannot explain this right, but this religion and their illness have something in common, like the texture of two tapestries, while other religions are not so, they are like linen or paint compared to it.

There is one man here who is continually searching for something in the toilet bowl, in a corner of l.is ward. He has his arm so deep in it that at times we can hardly get it out. He says his friend is down there. Also he talks through the barred window, never-ending poetry without rhyme and yet with a meter. His voice falls and rises with it and sometimes he yells the words. One poem I have remembered:

> The Cigarette Trees bloom over the clouds
> And Mainstreet looks like a melon,
> I am going to paint the battleships with Sarsaparilla,
> Do not forget me, the sun will melt this house.

He helps the Wardmaster in his ward, whenever one of the other patients gets out of hand. They are all violent cases and in this ward are only regular State Asylum men and the strongest. He is very strong, was a sergeant and killed an Officer in Europe. The attendants have allowed him to help in a pinch when they were hard up with two men fighting them, but the Irishman has warned them not to take help from the man with the toilet bowl, to watch that one.

The days are very short; the light changes early and at that hour the patients are depressed more than at any other time of the day; then also most of the fighting goes on and all of them walk around.

In this early evening I look out of the window and always wait for a certain little boy. He runs along home under the trees to a house at the end of the road, and in his thin legs and the little pants, fluttering in the wind, that hang down over them is the misery of all the world.

There is only tortured madness here, no single happy lunatic. In Tirol, in Uncle Hans's Hotel, we had a Maître d'Hôtel who one day became a happy case.

The Hotel stands high up on a mountain and is very elegant. The cogwheel railroad makes its last stop there. The name of the village is Klobenstein and the Hotel is named "The Old Post," *Die alte Post*. Further down, past the park and the tennis courts of the Hotel, is a low building, a peasant Inn; it has a little garden. We have a large one; our table clothes are white, theirs are colored with checks.

The Maître d'Hôtel always stands in front of the garden when the cogwheel railroad arrives, waits until the people come down, and smiles at them, bows, and seats them in the garden where they can eat and look at the scenery. The peasant Inn has no scenery as there are a hill and trees in front of it.

Uncle Hans first noticed that the Maître d'Hôtel was mad when one day he stood in front of the garden as the full train arrived and sent all the people down to the peasant Inn, saying we had no room, although the garden was completely empty and could seat over a hundred people. When one man with a family of six people, Prussians, but very well dressed, wanted to come in, the Maître d'Hôtel kicked him in the shins and shouted and sent him down to the peasant Inn. The little garden below was filled to bursting, they had not enough food and only one fat waitress. Some people could not find seats and started to come back, but the Maître d'Hôtel stood at the end of our hotel and picked up rocks. Then they sat inside the peasant Inn.

The next thing that happened, that same evening, was that he came into the salle à manger without even his shirt, stitch-naked, and chased Annie and the other servant girls around the room, which was filled with the regular "Pension" guests of the Hotel. Uncle called a Doctor, and the Maître d'Hôtel was locked in his room and put to bed. Uncle was very sad because this Maître d'Hôtel had been with us for twenty years.

In the morning he was gone. He had jumped out of his room through the window—curtain, glass, and all, without hurting himself—from the first floor, which is the second in America.

Aunt Marie was very proud of the Hotel park and gardens. They were neatly trimmed plots of greenery and flowers, bordered with rose trees and many fine plants, including tulips. This Maître d'Hôtel, although it was bitterly cold on top of the mountain in the morning, had used the early hours, working with great speed and the silver coupon shears from Uncle Hans's desk, to cut off every flower in the park. When we found him, he was on the second floor of the Hotel, hanging out of a balcony and cutting the geraniums in a window box next to the balcony. He had also cut them, stems, leaves, and all, on all the other windows. Uncle Hans took him by the arm and talked to him, and he answered reasonably, went to his room, and got dressed.

Because he had been with us for twenty years, Uncle Hans did not want to hurt him and gave him a good deal of money, after he was dressed and seemed allright again, and said: "Take a vacation, Herr Nolte." Nolte packed and took his money, but he came back again. In the village store he had spent all the money for every bottle of perfume he could get. This perfume was very bad, as it was bought for the peasants, that is, it smelled loud and of flowers, all sorts of them, sweet terrible scents assorted.

This he poured into himself in the reading room, into his overcoat pocket, into his bowler hat. He stuck a bottle, without the cork, upside down into his trousers and let the perfume run down there. He also drank it and rubbed some on his head, and all the time he cried and said: *"Ah, wie schön, wie gut, wie reichlich!"*—"Ah, how beautiful, how good, how plenty!" Then he took his clothes off, ran to the church, locked himself in, and rang the churchbells.

And that is the way, I thought, the patients in this Hospital should be, not sad but filled with highest spirits. I could never feel sorry for Nolte and had enough to amuse myself for months when I thought of him.

The Irishman was right about the man who searches in the toilet bowl. He bit through the throat of an attendant while he was helping put another man down. They had to beat him unconscious, six of them, ramming their elbows into his nose

and abdomen to get him loose while he shook all of them back
and forth between the walls. The attendant is in the Hospital.

A happy case has arrived at last, a sweet little patient whom
I liked at once. He comes into the Messhall for the first sitting.
We have so many patients that we have two meals three
times a day.

In the long double row of bent patients, he comes trotting
like a gay pony, hopping up and down and continually smil-
ing. He makes six hoppy steps to their one, and when he comes
to the column that holds up the ceiling in the middle of the
room, he dances around it, quick enough to be in his place
again while the others just pass.

Next he has a little ceremony for his stool. He hops around
it twice, shifts it into the right position back and forth, to the
left and right and once around, with one of its legs in a certain place. And when he is finally seated he carries his attention to the dishes, he rubs the plate on his nose in a circle, three
times, thereby giving it some power or just a greeting; then
he rubs the back of the spoon on his nose also three times, this
way and then the other way; then comes the cup, the bottom
of that and then the rim. He whispers a few words into the cup
and rubs it on the table. Then he mixes all the utensils and puts
them in order and looks around, quickly like a bird. He smiles
and nods several times as if to assent strongly to someone's
words. But he is also a bedwetter and must be called out in
the night.

My Bathstule Fint Porter

To the Left

AT three o'clock is a concert for the patients, to be held in a long, windy porch. Rows of benches have been placed, a platform faces them. Nina Morgana will sing; they say she is from the Metropolitan or will go there.

The men were walked in with all the attendants available; they stand at the sides of the benches. Almost one soldier, nurse, or guard for every four men.

They watched every motion of the singer with interest; it was a change from ward routine, but I doubt whether any of the men have heard much music, would know any of its values. They seem appreciative out of duty. There is no disturbance; the guards keep their eyes on the men; it would be disastrous if anything happened here, at least very dangerous, and it is very brave of Miss Morgana to come here.

53

With her are the Officers, and I thought it tactless that they somehow managed to give the impression that they and Miss Morgana belonged together and were much above both the patients and the soldiers. This was shown on their faces.

Tomorrow the men who take care of the patients, the attendants, will be examined. There seems to be danger of some of them getting ill themselves. The red Irishman tells me that in State Asylums the nurses get very long vacations and that a high percentage of them go mad in the end; also he says that all the Doctors are half mad. I have not been able to observe this myself; they are peculiar and there is a tendency to assume that they are not normal, which I think is a wish, not a fact.

We are being examined; two Doctors test reflexes, cover our eyes and then look into them quickly. We have to find the tip of our noses with the index finger of the right hand and eyes closed, and other such tests, also of course the knee test.

After we pass the Doctors, we are ordered to get into two lines, one on the right, one on the left. The line at the right is long, the one on the left very short. After a while, the ones at the left, with whom I am, are told to stay, and the right line is dismissed. I am fortunate for there is confusion while the dismissed pass by us, and I manage to leave with them, stepping out of my line.

I have done the better thing; the men at the left were again examined, more thoroughly so, and five out of twenty-four are being held back. They pack their things, and that evening they are in bathrobes at one of the tables in the patients' Mess and in a ward. Dreadful as it is, some of the other men have a hard time to conceal laughing at this.

No one, however, asks them anything, and they look down at their plates and feel ashamed. One of them in the middle of the meal throws his cup against the wall and sobs and then screams. The red Irishman is quickly behind him and holds him tightly. He fights, and then two more help to carry him out. My knees are weak, my hands not my own, I feel in danger.

Yesterday afternoon, as I walked across the parade ground, someone shouted my name loudly and right in back of my left shoulder. I turned and there was no one there, all around the mile-wide field.

I stood still motionless and with loud heartbeat; there was a bitter taste in my mouth and my hands felt loose again; so did my arms and my whole body, then hot and cold and wet, and tears came to my eyes.

Then I walked to my quarters and there again I heard my name called by the same voice, as distinct, and again in back of my left shoulder. I turned instantly—there was no one there again.

The barracks in which I live have a hall and a wide straight stairway leading up. This stairway started to turn itself around me in a yellow light. I fell.

Luckily no one saw this; I came to my consciousness again and slowly walked up and lay down on my bed.

In the last month two men in this room have jumped up in the night and became patients. I see them every day in the Messhall; I think they will not come out again.

For two hours I lay straight on my bed and looked at the ceiling. I thought of going to a doctor in Buffalo, but he might only give me away; besides all the psychiatrists are from Buffalo and work here, I would most probably run into one of our own men.

Also would I hold out as far as Buffalo? Now that the mind is loose from its moorings, I think it best to end my life rather than go into the wards. I have formed this plan; if only I can carry it through and hold on that long, because I am afraid to even move.

I know where the Guardhouse is, I know where the guns are. I will walk down the stairs, straight out the door, across the lawn and into the Guardhouse. There are men there, but I will manage to be plain so they will notice nothing, go into the lavatory with a gun that I will take from a holster, and then shoot up into my brain through the roof of the mouth.

I get up and start to walk down the stairs and out of my quarters with my mind fixed on this Must of death and afraid that a second of thinking, of reasoning, of hope, might mean weakness and change of mind.

I go out of the Barracks and fall over a cat and the cat does not run and everybody laughs loud.

An order had been issued the day before to get rid of all the cats, of which we have a plague. Two soldiers collected them all over the Fort and brought them back in their arms, then dropped them into an ashcan that is outside our Barracks. When they thought they had all the cats in there, they went to the Hospital and got four cans of ether and poured them in over the animals, then clamped the lid down, put a stone on it, and left. Some cat friend who did not like this came and took the stone off, upset the barrel, and the cats came out and regained consciousness.

They are wandering around in a stupor, lean against the ashcan, and look cross-eyed. Their motions are so funny, at

times like half wound up toys, at others, particularly the black
cats, who are wet with sweat and ether, they look like carica-
tures of cursed souls. None of them can stand up; it is so
strange and funny, everyone laughs; so must I, and it seems
so silly and useless to think that one might want to die.

I have never heard my name again although I have waited
for it, with a mind, inside my own, that is on watch all the
time and dreads this. The front mind does the duties and
thinks.

I have found a way to calm myself: I go myself to the
long baths. There is a bathroom for the men that is not much
used, as they prefer showers. I lie in it whenever I can, and I
have started to think in pictures and make myself several
scenes to which I can escape instantly when the danger appears.

These are all scenes from my childhood. Best of all, whenever the bitter taste, the tugging inside, and the prickly fear
in hands and temples arrives, is a walk from the Castle Tirol
down to Meran. I have taken this walk often. I remember
almost every tree and the turns of the road, the sound of the
churchbells from Meran below and from the village up above,
the light on the mountains at different times of the day and
the season.

I make it a practice to walk through Tirol every time I
am in danger. I start from the door of the Castle and go down
past the highest vineyards—there I place a little girl with bare
feet—to a field on the mountain slope, where oxen drag a
plow, and to an Inn, where I stop and sit down. I drink wine
and eat boiled chestnuts, and I have built all this with des-
perate detail and clarity and as if I were painting it. To this
end, the color of the red wine, the shape of the bottle in which

it comes, the pattern of the chairs and the table, the lamp and the foliage of the tree, are things that hold my mind and have to be thought about.

I go there in sunshine and in rain, in summer and in winter, to vary the play, to change the clothes, the room, the people. We are inside the Inn in winter. I people this room with the group of peasants that appear in Defregger's paintings and on the covers of the *Fliegende Blätter*. There are hunters with dachshunds and guns, gendarmes, children; and the detail of the room—with ivy growing out of pots high over the windows and running along the ceiling—the detail goes to flies, to the design on the buttons of the gendarmes. In all of this is protection, and time is gained; in this warm water is not only rest for the body, but for my mind, a bath for the soul.

In six days I have constructed six such Islands of Security: the Inn in Klobenstein, with the red sunset of the Dolomites and many people I love; a walk on the Danube from Regensburg, Bavaria, to Kelheim and a ride back on a slow train; a visit up and down to the Hungerburg, over Innsbruck in Tirol; a performance of a group of the Peasant Theater in Munich, and a visit to a small restaurant in back of the Church of Our Lady; also a ride in a landau through Munich and the English Gardens.

I intentionally think little of my brother, my mother, my friends, because in this I sense a bridge to the dangerous state. Pictures I want, instant happy pictures that are completely mine, familiar, warm, and protective.

I have bought some colored crayons, and make some of the sketches, but this is inadequate. The mental pictures are luminous, alive, and real, while the drawings are inadequate;

I always feel bad when I see many people do the same thing, that is, marching, playing, singing, particularly marching; and when I see children marching, and certainly so with a band, my eyes fill with tears, why I don't know.

After we have sung and eaten, there is a march around and after that more dancing; then the band plays "Good Night, Ladies," and it is over.

The soldiers have to go home alone. All the girls, even the unfortunate looking, are protected and taken away by parents or chaperones. They are all of nice or better people, and our men as they go home complain about not being able to get them. They say that very plainly and exchange their opinions as to how well it would be to have this or that one and why. They do that still in the dark in their beds, and the phrase usually is: "I betcha that blonde would be a good love," only a more direct word is used for "love."

I can talk now, particularly to Doris; her parents are German. They have a very feudal estate on the shores of the lake, several automobiles, servants and factories, also horses and a billiard room.

The chauffeur, who is also German, calls for me in the high Pierce Arrow car, and the food there is extremely good, also the wines, mostly good Moselle and Rhine wines. One of the rooms in this house is decorated like a Bierstube, and the old Gentleman head of the family is a Doctor, plain and elegant, and his wife is kind, motherly, and very plain in her dress. We speak mostly, in German, of Germany, of Munich, of the Rhine, also of Meran and Tirol. I think the war makes him sad and he is glad a soldier who is a German visits him.

On Sundays when the sun is out we go riding, and when it

rains we sit in the house and read. Doris is proud of having a soldier. There seem to be no Officers around or at least none she likes better, and she says that, if we wanted to get married, her father would do nothing about it, because I am in the Army and an American Soldier and Citizen. Also because I am German it would make him happy anyway, and so it would be pleasant all around, but nothing became of it, because I was afraid to ask her.

There is much work at the Fort, new patients have arrived, many of them, new barracks are going up, the kitchens are enlarged, and the Messhalls made twice as big as they were. Everyone is working very hard.

What with this work, the Rabbi Kopald, the parties and Doris, her horses and the country, the fear has almost gone and appears only in the middle of the night when I awake trembling and wet from toes to the top of my head. But now I am so well trained that even without preparation and the bath I can hang my pictures over the terror, quickly, and blot it out.

The great misfortune is over there in the Hospital. Instead of locking the patients up together, marching them around to the ugly Messhalls where they must be quiet, and then having them sit on their beds all day long, where they are stuck in misery and illness, and when this overcomes them fighting them down, if each one could be taken away alone with somebody who cared and taught them how to think their way out of this, they might be helped. That is the hopelessness of the Asylum. They should be far away from it, from their own kind, and if they have no good memories to think of, then the present should be made happy and light for them. Their cure need only be a landscape, a decent person, even a dog or a horse, but it should be some one thing they can love outside of themselves. But of course I cannot see myself how this could be put into practice.

Uncle Joseph and his Dog

Tirol in Buffalo

By accident somebody left a wooden crate, in which oranges are delivered, in the baking part of the oven last night, and in the morning it was toasted without being burned. It was made of thin pine wood, and when I came into the kitchen, I felt heartsick because it smelled just like my sawmill in Tirol.

When I close my eyes and smell a little piece of wood which I have broken off the crate, I can see the mill, the road that leads to it, the water that comes in through the roof. This water

65

runs along in a narrow wooden river that is carried along on heavy beams and sometimes built onto strong trees. This is done to keep it high and then give the water much drop, so that, when a wooden partition is pulled out, it shoots down through the roof onto the wheel that is thirty feet high and begins to turn it.

Not all the water goes that way; some of it is left below in the bed of the brook. This water is crystal clear, the bed is covered with fine sand; ferns and waterplants stand in it, and little lizards, jet black with flaming carmine patches, also many frogs, green as grass, with golden eyes. And little fishes live there.

In the valley stand the highest pines. The road winds in and out on the mountain side, only teams of oxen can go along to drag the heavy loads; they are slow but much stronger than horses, and the wagons they pull have two little wheels in front and long beams that drag along and act as a brake, because the road is very steep and always changes up and down.

Over the entrance of the mill is a statue of the Lord; He sits resting His chin in His arm and is very sad. The statue, like all the Christuses along the road, and there are many of them, is the work of a peasant artist. The artists have made the Christuses so earnestly that the suffering they themselves felt has gone over into the wood. They carve on them their own faces, and they are beautiful, honest, simple, and look sorry for the whole world. The design is not always good; the dimensions are wrong—sometimes they are a little too fat, or the legs are not long enough—the part from the knee to the ankle is very hard for them to carve.

Because of this, the statues are humble, and each one, with his little house around it, which is seen only in Tirol **and**

Austria, is a private, different Christus and much stronger than the good, heroic ones that are too beautiful and too much alike.

At the base of all these Christuses are flowers from the fields that peasants put there—the lovely yellow cowslips, blue gentians, crocuses—willows, and, in the winter, pine branches.

The trees here about, and they are almost all pines, are free of branches almost to the top. This is because the peasants are poor; they cut the branches up to a height of thirty feet, trim the wood in the center for fire, and use the small ends with the needles for the stables. That is why the stables here smell so lovely.

No one believes me that the cattle on the high mountains have much more intelligent faces than in the valleys. This is also true of the people, even of their dialect. In the narrow valleys they are sullen and gruff and hardly speak; up above is more sun, lighter air, high voices, and much room, and they are happier, sing and dance. And the cattle grazing along dangerous precipices must think more; the oxen and the cows have serious and beautiful faces; they are also better in construction and much cleaner.

The finest place to see all this is on the hill in back of the mill, with the water flowing into the roof and coming out as spray below, with the sound of the wheel turning. From here a whole world can be seen—houses far below, little and littler; a church on the mountain opposite with a tower sharp as the point of a pencil, its bells clearly heard. Behind it soaring into the sky is the ring of mountains that change colors all day long and are glowing purple and carmine when the sun sets. All this I see with the little piece of wood under my nose. I can even ride back to the hotel with it and see the German tourists who always stand in groups, after they have written postal cards, and argue about the names of the mountains. They do that with printed panoramas in their hand, pointing and get very mad. They don't believe even our head waiter and look into the Baedeker to see if he is right about the height of each mountain.

The cogwheel railroad that runs from Bozen up the Ritten, to the last station, which is Klobenstein, has an electric locomotive. The car is a streetcar, really, that runs through Bozen and up on the mountain under its own power, but when it takes the long steep mountain climb, the little locomotive gets behind it and a man attaches three different safety couplings. Then the conductor blows a little trumpet that sounds: "Baehh," and the car tilts upward, and slowly it moves up, very slowly. I have found out that when I call long distance on the telephone the same sound as that on the locomotive, a howling, electric noise, is heard. Therefore when I get very homesick, instead of forgetting about it, I call long distance to hear this and then hang up.

I think if anybody would find out in this place about the little piece of pine wood which I heat and smell and the long distance calls for no purpose, I might have difficulty.

When the danger is of the worst kind, then my safest Island is Uncle Joseph. He cannot hear. He is up on the mountain and a simple peasant priest, and people from far away come to him because he is so good, and to confess to him because it is much easier. He watches their lips and forgives everything when they stop talking.

He has a little dog of no race, salt and pepper colored, with short legs, ears like a bat, and a face like a very old disgusted man. With this dog Uncle Joseph takes his daily prayer walk, with a little book out of which he reads. He always carries an

umbrella that swings in back of him as if he had wheels inside
and it were the pendulum. He speaks little, I think, because he
feels that nobody can hear him either, but when he speaks he
says everything very loud. Mostly he speaks with his eyes. He
must be seventy years old, but he is very hale and sometimes,
for no reason, on a long walk, he skips and jumps a few steps
and then turns around to smile. He has permission from the
Pope to wear a beard, because he has a goiter, but in Tirol a
goiter is something almost to be proud of, because all the
peasants have them and therefore speak with a deep basso.

The dog is also very old; he does not go to trees any more,
and when he has to stop, he just spreads his four legs with his
little belly on the ground and makes water and, doing this,
his lips tremble and he looks more miserable than he does
all the time.

When Uncle Joseph sees a little flower along the road, he
stops and silently points at it, or at a bird in the air, and again
smiles. He is a holy man. On Sunday in his little church he
preaches, and when a peasant comes in late, he stops the
sermon and speaks to him from the pulpit, and it is the only
time I know that he gets mad. He points up to the ceiling of
the church and speaks for the Father in heaven and says:
"Franzl, where have you been again?" The peasant is then
ashamed and hides behind a pillar, and after the service when
Uncle Joseph walks through the church with holy water and
a silver-handled brush to bless them, he takes an extra large
dip and rains it on that peasant.

Uncle Joseph has other troubles. He has very little money, he
lives plainly, all he can spare he gives to the poor or to many
causes.

Another is the painting of the Christuses. There is a very

good religious man with a beautiful white beard, who is a house painter and carpenter, and he has also to go around during the year and paint the many statues so they will not be eaten by the strong air, the heavy snow, and the cold. This man tries very hard to do this right, and when one watches him paint, he mirrors the face of the statue on his own. He is so deeply attached to this work. He does it the way children paint, with the mouth tightly closed, but unfortunately he is a very bad artist.

First of all, he mixes a terrible color for the statues; it is too red, and sickly red, as in a fever, or too pale, yellowish, and then the worst thing is that, when he comes to the face, he sometimes makes the eyes not right. All his Christuses have bad eyes; some of them are cross-eyed, and others look away to both sides at the same time. And then he cannot make the mouth sad; this is very bad, because some of the Christuses almost smile.

When Uncle Joseph comes to a newly painted one, after he has removed his hat, which on warm days he carries on a clip in a buttonhole in front of his chest, he points at it and shakes his head; but he is too kind to say anything to that man or to have someone else do it.

On these walks, little girls in wide skirts and flaxen hair come running out of houses, and make a curtsy and kiss his hand, and they say: "Praise to God in heaven," and Uncle Joseph blesses them with his hand on their hair and answers: "In Eternity, Amen."

This fills me always with an inner trembling, and a warm love for him, and, although I cannot believe in his religion, in the evenings, when he goes through the deep forests to a dying peasant and in his folded arms carries the Host, the altar

boy ahead of him swinging a little lamp and ringing a silver
bell, then I know, with certainty, more than I know anything,
that he is of God.

GARDEN IN GMUNDEN.
SALZKAMMERGUT.

David

LIEUTENANT DOYLE and the Chaplain have arranged for out-
ings for the patients. On certain days cars will come to the
Fort; in them will be one patient and one attendant; then they
will all drive in one long line to the country and make a tour
for fresh air, coming back again in several hours.

Lists are made out, so that this can be done properly. I manage to arrange with the Sergeant clerk, who writes out these
lists, that Doris will drive my patient; his name is David.

David is a young Negro; he sits quiet and content in a chair
and looks down on the floor, at all times, straight ahead of his
chair. He has on his young face a constant smile; his face is of
distinguished and fine formation and for his race I think one
of the best, purest.

73

He never says anything, but when he is given something, he looks at it intently as if he has never seen it before, for a long, long time. He thanks you with a nod and with his eyes and goes back to the quiet smile and the stare. He looks forever as if he were posing for a black statue of St. Anthony.

Because a strong wind blows in from the lake, David gets a warm cover over his bathrobe, and over this a coat. Doris brings a two-seater; he sits between us after we are checked out. All through the long drive he looks at the spot where the clutch comes out of the floorboards, never at the country.

On the third such round ride, Doris brought him some chocolate, for which he thanked her with silent, great dignity. Also there are a pair of big fur mittens to put on his hands because it is very cold in the open car. We have to stop to put them on and in this time the train of cars with patients passes us and is far ahead.

The regulations forbid this, but we drive our own way, out to the country. It is nicer; we can go faster and it is more fun than continually watching the car ahead. We come to many nice places and stop at one to walk through the wood. David we leave in the car and we make him comfortable with a blanket. It is a quiet deserted road.

We were not far at any time, or gone long. When we came back and looked into the car, David was gone. Doris ran to the right, I to the left; we shouted his name into the woods and fields; there was no sign of David.

This will surely mean the Guardhouse; it's a serious offense, even if David is not dangerous, or perhaps he is, very much so, and has only been waiting for this moment.

We climbed into the car. There he was, the top of his head stuck up over the side. He was sitting out on the running board where we had never looked, his hands folded on his lap, with the saint's smile.

After this they did not let us take him out again. The committee crossed Doris and her car off the list. I was reprimanded, and David went out in another car with another attendant.

I can visit him in his ward, bring him custard and chocolate, and feed it to him. His Doctor says he is not getting any better, and in another week he is put to bed.

Davy is very ill; he looks straight ahead of himself, somewhere about twelve feet in front of his face, and seems smaller. His hands rest silently and loose at the sides of his body. It is feared he will die. The young Doctor whom I like and who is very kind to David has little hope for him. He seems not to want to live, and late one night he almost dies.

The Doctor took gloves of rubber and with his forefinger reached up into the sick boy's backside. There must be a nerve center there, because he reacted and almost sat up straight. Then two days later his breathing changed and in the middle of the night he died. It is not sad though it is the first time I have seen it happen.

When I was very little, a stupid nurse took me on Sunday afternoon to the cemetery. Behind great windows lay the dead, and among them the one I will always see, a very little, old, old Countess. Her feet were in thin paper shoes; two candles burned at the sides of her plain, black, wooden coffin; her little hands were folded over a black crucifix; and between their fingers were wound the beads of a rosary.

I have never been able to forget this, because her eyes were wide open, a fly circled over her face and landed in the middle of the eye; the fly walked around over the staring pupil, and

I waited for the face to move. But the little lady was so dead that the fly was undisturbed; it walked down the bridge of the nose, into one of the nostrils, came out again, and left the face.

That seemed complete death to me and made me angry. The cemetery was on a hill over the town; it was filled with broken columns, weeping stone angels, crosses, big and small, white and black, and young trees. It was raining; the bells of the mortuary chapel had a high homeless sound; in the hall, behind the large windows where the dead lie on view, stood several people, curious and staring. Against the walls leaned flags, lanterns, and a crucifix on a long pole; all this was used for the funerals, and the most ugly of all things was the smell of cooking that drifted into this corridor from the end of the hall where lived the caretaker. It was Sunday, and the smell was of goulash, coffee, and beer.

The Countess was so very dead to me because I had seen her alive. I lived at the time alone with a French nurse in a little walled garden in Gmunden on the shore of the Traunsee, in the Salzkammergut.

Although we were in Austria and I was five years of age, I could hardly speak German. On the waters were swans, many white, a few black; in the garden stood immense chestnut trees that formed a green roof over it. And the little old lady fitted so well into this; she wore a black velvet ribbon on her thin neck, stood and sat straight, and had the character of a turtle in her face. That of course was the wrinkly skin, a proud mouth without lips, and the nostrils that leaned back. Ugly as she was, I loved her. She spoke beautiful French, had in her appearance a commanding little General's military correctness and elegance. I remembered her in all her motions.

But David's death was not like this.

There is a man in the Fort who apparently has no duty to perform; he is never asked to drill or put on the guard detail. He is a Corporal and, now that we have a dead soldier, he appears to be the undertaker.

David is in a room; he lies naked on a table and the undertaker is draining the blood from his body and pumping some liquid into it. He sits at the head and feels David's ear, to see if it is getting stiff.

In the evening David is most beautiful; he has the form of a statue, much finer than any white man I have ever seen. Blue lights play over his body; the part from the chest to his knees is the finest; even his organs are well designed, small, compact and part of his loins. His legs and arms look strong, as if polished steel were covered with a thin layer of cloudy wax, opaque, yet transparent. It is a fine pleasure to look at him; he does not look at all dead.

I have watched some operations in Oswego on colored men. When their abdomens are opened, there is snowy whiteness inside for several centimeters, and only when the surgeon cuts down deeper, does the dark blood come up and fill the cut.

The knowledge of Anatomy explains David's body. I know little of it but enough to respect its wonder. I know where heart, lungs, intestines are, where the bones lead to and where they are joined. The forms of all this can be felt through his skin.

I go to him as often as I can, just to stand and look at his death. He never ceases to be young and strong, and somehow there is consolation in this room, it is like some of the music of the Bruch Concerto.

The soldiers are decent. It is the first death in the Hospital;

they take it seriously and play taps for him, give him an escort and drape his flag over the coffin. One man has to take him home. They all seem sad to me, their mothers' children, and very small. This is most evident in the way they dress and clean their shoes and are quiet for David.

The
messhall
FORT PORTER.

The Mess in Order

I HAVE been given the management of the Mess, that is, under Lieutenant Doyle. I have also no worry with buying food or supplies; that is the business of the Quartermaster Sergeant. We feed many patients and soldiers, all together almost two thousand people. The patients' Messhall is separated and in another building. The Messhall for the men is here close to the kitchen.

79

The cooks are good men. One of them is English and thin; he speaks a wonderful Cockney dialect, and says he has to make himself a "heggnogg." We have lots of cockroaches; they crawl to the ceiling, so at night the windows and doors are left open and they freeze to death and are swept out in the morning, but there are new ones the next day; also again those many cats everywhere.

In other posts there are periodic assignments of all men to Kitchen Police, but here, because of the nature of this house, we have a steady crew, men who cannot be used for better work, and they are difficult.

These men are all friends; they come from the Brooklyn waterfront, were drafted. The worst one is Mulvey.

Mulvey sings all day, so that his song—it is the same one—has become part of the kitchen, like the cooks and the oven. We cannot drive it out. It is a dreary piece and he draws it out, singing mostly into the dishwater. The words go:

> Take me over the Sea—
> That's where I want to be—
> Oh, my, I don't want to die,
> Take me over the Sea.

There is also something about "I want to go home" in it.

His friends join him in that line while they are busy with their dishes. These come in endless stacks all day long, after breakfast, luncheon, and dinner.

They love to insult each other in play and call themselves by the vilest names, all in fun; and at times, while the water is running into the tub or they are waiting for the towels to dry, they box without touching each other, dancing on their toes and, at the most, disarranging their opponent's hair. In their free hours they are visited by girls that are as terrible as they themselves are—ragged women, young enough, but with thick ankles, in shoes with blunt toes and sideway heels, with pimply faces, wide hips, and fat lips. With them they sit on a row of benches facing the river. But they are always together and behave toward the rest of us with great condescension, as if they belonged to an exquisite club that is very hard to get into. So far as I have seen, all they do out there with the girls is sing again this song, sit on the benches where they insult each other, and shout the same insults of short words after anyone who passes. Their girls sit with knees far apart and love to be pushed and mauled; they scream with happiness.

The Ideas of morality that people have seem so confusing. The men here are all so lonesome; the kitchen gang knows nothing else but to box and this business of which they constantly talk by one word. And after all it is only the itch that is in their bodies which marches in front of the command to have more people on earth, and of course they don't want any children, but it itches them just as hard. But these thoughts always confuse me, and I think of women, of girls I have seen at dances and swimming, and most I think of the muscles that run down to the knees on the inside of their upper leg; they are I think the most exciting part, much more so than any other part of their bodies, in young girls most certainly, in women they become flabby, and of porous texture.

When the kitchen gang are through washing the dishes, they have to set the tables in the Messhall. After meals, the three-legged stools on which the men sit are turned upside down and placed on top of the tables so that the floor can be mopped. These stools are taken down; then one man runs through the lanes between the tables and places the plates from a pile on his arm. He does this fast from much practice. The plates dance awhile and then settle down. The next one runs around with forks, another with spoons, knives, and another with tin cups. One can hear with little experience what they are doing without being in the room. There are, of course, no napkins.

For some time there have been complaints that the dishes are greasy. They do not wash them well enough, the same with knives and forks and the cups. The Officer in charge took a clean towel, slipped the end of it between the prongs of a fork, and showed me how dirty it became. He streaked a plate with his glove and, tilting it in the light, the path of his finger could be seen across the plate—it was fatty.

I told this to Mulvey, out in the kitchen. He turned from his tub and looked at me with small eyes; he has a way of making them look perfidious. Also, when he is told something, he assumes a position of great ease, leaning on the edge of the dishwashing tub and crossing his legs, his body as in a hammock, leaning toward me. With his free hand he scratches himself. This performance is chiefly for his friends, who stand around him and have great admiration for such a show of indifference.

After I have told him all this, he has to turn around and go on with his work, and he does it very slowly, looking into the faces of all his friends, taking a deep breath, and he says as if he were very tired: "Oh—well." He spits in the dishwasher and continues to wash the dishes in it.

I am sorry I cannot box, but I will not allow him to get away with this. The next day is Saturday and there is a football game; they love football games; their terrible girls always

come for them and hang around the front of the Messhall.
They hurry on that day and don't sing, and I will teach them
a lesson. Before they can go off duty, they must ask me for
permission.

The best part of this Saturday afternoon is that, when they
have almost finished the dishes and started to set the tables, the
top Sergeant, the Polish one, comes in late and eats in the
kitchen. They are afraid of him; he has a voice like a bear,
can beat them up one and all together, and on top of it lock
them in the Guardhouse until their bones ache.

I walked into the dining room after the tables were all set,
and one of them came to ask if they could go. Mulvey was
already out of the door. Of course they could go if everything
was done, but everything was not done, not right. I showed
them the dirty forks and the greasy plates. Mulvey was called
back. I made them take all the dishes and cups, the forks,
spoons, and knives back, to wash them over again. They still
thought they could make the game.

Mulvey used steaming water and raced around the room
to help them. The plates danced down again, the top Sergeant
nodded to me, the men were mumbling curses, audible enough
for me to understand that they were not insulting each other.
When they were finished they asked again to go.

I pointed at the tables and stools. "What is this?" I said.
"Look at it, what a disorder! And the plates and the forks!"

Mulvey was sent to get a long string and two pieces of wood.
The top Sergeant leaned against the door of the dining room
and grinned, with his hands in his pocket.

The string came, and with a pencil I divided the first and
last table in each row of tables in as many places as there were
men sitting at them. Then we put the first and last tables in

correct position, laid the string over the row of ten tables on each side, and first of all pushed the tables so that they were absolutely straight. The Polish Sergeant helped by bending to the edge of the first table and closing one eye, like looking down the line of stomachs of soldiers. He gave a signal with his hand for each table until they were quite in line.

Then with the string we aligned all the stools, the plates and cups of each man, also straightened out the knives and forks.

When this was done, I told them now they could go and from now on we would do it like this at every meal. By that time it was time for supper. But they ran out to their girls who had waited.

After supper they again hurried and set the tables. I felt sorry for them.

I went up to my quarters to get the leather leggins to go out. We can wear spiral puttees, if we buy them, but not leather leggins. We should, however, according to regulations, wear the canvas leggins which are furnished by the service.

Uniforms we can also have our own; I had one made in Buffalo. There is only the terrible campaign hat; no one is allowed to wear a cap or hat like the Officers have, but I have bought myself a Stetson campaign hat which at least holds its shape and has a somewhat better color. Besides it does not turn up at the corners like a cooked mushroom.

My leather leggins, which are forbidden, I have in a bag and, carrying it under my arm, I leave the Fort. Next to the Fort is a park, and there is a bush where I sit down and change the canvas for the leather leggins and hide the canvas ones until I get back. I have also spurs in my pocket. When this is done, I wait for Doris's big car. It is a Pierce Arrow with the front seats apart so one can walk between them from the back seat and sit with the driver.

As I sat down under the bush, a blanket fell on me, and then I was hit on the head by a plank. It was from the kitchen gang. They kicked and trampled with boots and clubs until I was insensible. I woke up in the Hospital and could not see out of my eyes; my head swam and all my limbs hurt.

I sent for the Polish Sergeant and asked him to have the kitchen gang arrested. He gave me a chocolate bar and said No, he would not do that, because I had it coming to me. "It will do you good," he said, "this is America."

The Buttermachine

THERE are two Doyles here—one a Sergeant, the other a Lieutenant. The Sergeant is efficient and thin; the Lieutenant is fat, with the face of an old lady and little eyes that easily turn hard with offense. He always looks past my face when he speaks to me. The soldiers have invented a very right and beautiful name for him—his trousers have given them this idea—they call him "Satchel Ass." A "satchel" is a portmanteau and "ass" is a donkey but in this case it is the army word for derrière—it fits well. When he walks, it looks as if this portmanteau were constantly opened and closed, and when he sits down, it flows over the chair. When he has been around,

87

they do not say: "Lieutenant Doyle was here"; they say: "Doyle was here." Question: "Which one?" Answer: "Satchel Ass Doyle."

Lieutenant Doyle is the Glee Club leader and Mess Officer. He complains all day long about the flies, looks into the ice-machine and the iceboxes, and his pet is the buttermachine. He looks at it twice a day with affection. He bought it himself and he shows all the other Officers or some friends of his that come visiting how it works. "That's a great little piece of machinery there," he says to them.

The buttermachine has been here ten days. Before that we cut the butter with a small square frame over which a row of thin sharp wires were stretched, making about sixteen squares. These wires run from left to right and up and down. One man and a tub of water with ice is all that is needed to cut all the butter for the men, the patients, and even the Officers' Mess; and all this takes is at the most ten minutes.

Now we have to first rinse the buttermachine with hot water, fill it with ice, then trim the blocks of butter, because as they are they do not fit the round cylinder inside the ice. The cylinder is long and round, the blocks of butter are square and short. One and a half of them, after they are trimmed, fit into the machine. When they are in there, a tight cover is attached, the heavy lid clamped down, and then the work begins.

A man has to stand in front of the machine and work a little lever from left to right and back again to the left; and every time these two motions are completed, one little square of butter falls out of the machine.

I have told Lieutenant Doyle that it is a waste of time, that the butter was cut in ten minutes before and now it takes two

hours to do it, and twice a day; it is ridiculous. But he says:
"That buttermachine is allright."

I have detailed Mulvey, who is the laziest of the K.P.'s,
to this work, and he is now in the dining room and sings his
awful song in there and makes these little butterpieces. Mulvey
soon finds out that, with making a little fuss, he can stretch
his work so that he has nothing else to do, and when Lieutenant
Doyle comes in and sees him cleaning the machine very carefully, he stops and smiles and he tells me: "Mulvey is a good
man." But I will fix that.

We have one Mess table that has a broken leg. After mid-
day meal, when the dishes are washed, would be a good time
to do this, but then there are too many people and I think such
things should always be done alone with no one around for
confusion when somebody asks questions later on.

Sunday is the best day, then all is very quiet, everyone is out.
On the next Sunday, when I am not invited out until late in the
evening, I move the table with the broken leg over to the door
and change it for the one on which the buttermachine sits.
This one has good legs. There is a corner of the table which
meets the door when it is opened—soldiers rush into rooms—
and on that corner is the machine. It is very heavy, about one
hundred and fifty pounds.

After this is arranged, I go up to my quarters. There was a
crash as soon as I got up there, but I dressed and left, because
it was time to meet Doris's car.

The next day when I am back in the Messhall, the cook says:
"Somebody busted the buttermachine. Lieutenant Doyle is
wild and wants to see everybody who works here."

The best thing is to go right over to headquarters and look

surprised and make a face that asks: "Who could have **done** this? Let me think."

Mulvey is there already answering questions. The butter-machine is there also, but I am afraid that it can be repaired; one of the pig iron legs is broken off, and the machinery under the cylinder, where the lever goes back and forth and the butter comes out, seems mangled, but it looks good otherwise.

Lieutenant Doyle has no suspicion; he points at the machine and says: "What do you think of that?" but he asks no more. Mulvey has told him when he saw the machine last and another man how he found it. Whoever opened the door and broke it is not to be determined because he would not report himself and no one has seen anybody else.

All questions and answers are filled out on a long printed statement which the Army issues for all things that break or are lost or worn out. Mulvey is back washing dishes and we cut the butter the old way for some weeks. Then Lieutenant Doyle comes and takes Mulvey away from the dishwashing. He comes back with a small table with very strong legs. Lieutenant Doyle has picked out a corner where to put it; near this corner are no doors. Outside is a truck, with a new butter-machine.

François, Marie Arouet de Voltaire

1694 — 1778

Night on Guard

THE Flu Epidemic has cost many lives and it is to keep the men that work here well that we are changed from one duty to another.

Yesterday the red-headed Irishman and I were working in the Post Hospital carrying the dead men down to the cellar on stretchers. We wear long white nurse's gowns and a cap,

91

also a pad over mouth and nose and look like ghosts. The cellar stairs turn and are very steep.

The Irishman was in front of me, walking ahead down, when the dead man slipped and his feet went into the Irishman's back. He said: "Sit down or I knock you down!" This kept me from screaming or dropping the body.

Down in the cellar is a room and in this we have brought the corpses. The Irishman takes the feet when we lift them off, I take them by the hair as I do not wish to touch their faces or neck, which is stupid of me, but the hair is better, it is not so dead. The post undertaker now has a lot of work, he has the assistance of several undertakers from Buffalo. I wonder if he has a girl.

There are not enough men to mount guard, the posts are reduced, and although I am a Corporal I must stand guard.

The third night I am down in the cellar again, now as a night guard. The dead must be watched, there is a regulation to this effect, they cannot be left alone.

The cellar is dark and lit by a loose gas flame, this flame is on the outside of the room where the dead are. They lie in rows and no one has had time to close their eyes. In the white of these eyes dances the reflection of the gas light. I sit as close to the wall as I can squeeze myself and I am terribly afraid, so afraid that I have taken my gun out of its holster and point it at the dead men. The safety catch is off and it makes me feel safe. If anyone of them will move, I'm afraid I'll kill him, I don't see why they cannot be left alone, or locked up over night, or why there aren't at least two of us.

The Epidemic is much better and almost over; now I have

an altogether new duty. I am stationed at the Guardhouse and I see that the men who have been on leave report for inspection before turning in. They come in at all hours of the night. Some of them have late passes, which I have to collect as well.

After all the soldiers are inspected and have gone to bed, when everybody except a few men out on posts are asleep, I have time to myself.

After the reports are in order, I read, mostly Voltaire, Goethe, a little book of Schiller's poems, and on Napoleon.

Later I go out; the air is so cold that it bites inside the nose, and when I come back I am much thinner.

It is also difficult to walk because the roads are icy, and at times I must quickly slide to a tree, or the wind would take me along across the frozen parade ground.

The clouds race past the moon; there are more stars than I have ever seen in America. In the metallic light, the roofs of the Hospital buildings seem to float in the air in one flat green-silver row of tilted panels; under them the Hospital is quiet most of the time. At times there is a scream from the bad section and then the figure of a nurse passes the lit windowpane, but that happens not very often.

Around the Fort is water, lit as the roofs are, and in this scene is a dangerous ecstasy, an elation which begins as the fear does. It swells up in back of me, high and wide, and as if I were standing in front of an orchestra with rows of instruments wildly playing.

In this excitement many doors open to walk out of the house of reason. The mind becomes acutely clear. This goes through the body, as if the brain, the fingertips, all surfaces, were sandpapered and the nerves laid bare to every sensation. The mind was a little cup and now it is as big as a tub. This happens every night. First of all I feel years older, and whatever I think seems crystal clear. Also I seem able to do anything.

I have had this feeling mildly before, when coming out of a motion picture in which the acrobatic hero has swung himself on a curtain up the side of a tower and jumped on horseback across the parapets. For half an hour afterwards I have felt like doing the most difficult things in play, to jump, to take hold of anything and swing myself up to the next electric sign on Broadway, to successfully punch anybody in the nose that seemed not worth liking.

Here, now that the Islands of Security are where I know I can reach them, there is the constant wish to walk out further on the thin plank of reason, to gamble with the chance of not being able to come back.

The highest joy, and it is always a boundless happiness, is when the sun rises. It remains resting on the horizon for a long while and then frees itself, floats freely. I feel then a sense of the miraculous logic and divine bookkeeping that makes all things in this world a day older—myself, my mother, the sawmill, the patients, the dead grass under the snow, the trees—and for all these things wells up a rich affection, so that I must put my arms around a tree and feel its being. I also feel the sun, where it has been, with unbelievable detail—the shadows it has thrown past the church in Klobenstein, on the Christuses, on Uncle Joseph who is out with his dog, on the ventilators of the ships on the ocean, and here now on the snow past this tree.

Shortly before the sunrise there is a blue light all over, somewhat like in a theater, where they change the light from night to morning too fast. Unreal, humid and inky, and spattered with yellow street lamps; when you squint your eyes, the street-lights rain gold over the scene. In this light a milk wagon horse clops up the street and a man who has to go to work early comes out of a house always in the same fashion: he yawns, closes his collar, and lets a small dog out after him. He walks down the steps and sees me and lifts his hand in greeting, and then, and always in this same order, bends down to speak to his dog. The ill-formed, unkempt, many-kinds-of-dog makes a creaky sound, scrapes and scratches, and is beside himself with gratitude. He shows this with all his might, wiggling so that one moment his head looks at his tail on the right side of his body and then on the left. It is his daily morning prayer to his master and for himself to show how glad he is to be alive and how grateful to be a dog.

Then the sun rises, it places light on ice-covered branches and on a young oak leaf that has stuck through wind and winter. It is curled like the webbed claw of a bird and becomes liquid and gilded.

Then the prisoners arrive; they go from the Guardhouse to the Messhall to get food. They are dressed in the wonderful fatigue suit, blue with the lovely large Prison "P" handpainted on its back, and they have the foolish fatigue hat—fatigue is so right for this. They also show their prisonness in their walk. Behind them goes the guard; they all hurry to get into the warm kitchen, to warm their hands. I always follow them and love their walk, their faces, their words. Hat, coat, tray, all speak. They say: "We are prisoners, not bad fellows. We only drunk too much, or fought, and it's nice in the jail, but hurry up, kitchen, so we can get a little coffee and sit by the oven." The guard is much less eloquent.

In the kitchen they look around to swipe something from

the cook. They get an extra cup of coffee here. The cook is the thin low-class Englishman, with the lovely London dialect. He is simpleminded, and in all simple people is a securing, restful quality. When he looks in a pot, I can read on his face whether it is clean or dirty inside.

There are some specialists, who have a right, or just a claim of their own invention, to a cup of coffee here early. Their faces appear on the side of the door, and they look at the cook, to find out whether he is in the right mood, if he will give it to them.

In all this, the appearance of the horse, the little dog, the prisoners, and the cook, is wonder without end. In them also are the strongest weapons against illness of the mind, against even just a low mood. There is an ever present quiet humor; one must only sit and listen carefully and look for it, but of course I think one must have been very ill to be so grateful. I am no longer afraid. After breakfast I go over to the Guardhouse to sleep. If the danger comes, it is now controlled. Physically it is the same—quickly changing temperature, fast pulse and respiration, cold sweat and bitter running of water down the inside of the cheeks—but mentally it is much better. It is now about the same sensation I have when looking into a shopwindow of artificial limbs, or when seeing an ugly child weep somewhere alone.

Another experience like the sunrise is Voltaire, who is again so vivid; himself, his clothes, Sans Souci, Frederick the Great, the affair with the diamonds, are all alive as if he were sitting over in the Headquarters building. Sentences of his malicious sacred writing are before me, clear and free as if I could read them in fine letters on the façade of a marble temple. He is for me clarity, truth, and highest freedom of thought. Because I must return the book, I have copied a picture out of it, a good bust of Voltaire. I wish I could paint. I carry it with me always. I have also drawn what I think Thunder-ten-tronckh, Cunégonde, and the wonderful Dr. Pangloss look like, but torn them up because they were poor.

Doris has sent me *The Italian Voyage* of Goethe, and mountain stories of Tirol by Peter Rosegger. I cannot keep my mind on any of this, with all the disturbance that this new duty brings. I will have to replace *The Italian Voyage,* because yesterday I pushed a bottle with ink over and it made a big splotch in the book; besides it smells already of this place.

In the book of Poems by Friedrich von Schiller is "The Song of the Bell," a long ode without feathers in its wings. The books lie next to each other, but of course it is unfair to compare Schiller with Voltaire. But in Germany, Schiller's poetry is so eminent and compulsory that if one will say to a little boy, to a soldier, a lady washroom attendant, or a streetcar conductor, or any German rich or poor, anywhere in this world: *"Festgemauert in der Erde,"* or any other sentence from "The Song of the Bell," the so addressed will take it from there and recite it to its faraway end, in the rigid form that has been carved into his mind and voice on the first schoolbenches.

In German one cannot say the elegant candle-lit phrases. My affection for German is that which one gives to a box full of cobbler's tools; they are not always well used when speaking, for example Schiller in his "Ode to Joy":

> *Seid umschlungen, Millionen!*
> *Diesen Kuss der ganzen Welt!*
> *Brüder, über'm Sternenzelt*
> *Muss ein lieber Vater wohnen.*

This word *umschlungen* is better suited for a lady at a Fair with a snake around her; *diesen Kuss der ganzen Welt* is hurtful; and *Brüder* is a word that belongs better in a restaurant, as, for example: *"Trink, trink, Brüderlein, trink."* Even worse is this from Schiller's "Song of the Bell":

> *Von der Stirne heiss*
> *Rinnen muss der Schweiss,*
> *Soll das Werk den Meister loben;*
> *Doch der Segen kommt von Oben.*

I like German words best when a simpler man uses them; for example, the good Wilhelm Busch writes:

> *Links sind Bäume, rechts sind Bäume,*
> *Und dazwischen Zwischenräume,*
> *Durch die Mitte der Natur*
> *Zieht sich eine Pappelschnur.*

In this humble, humorous employment the German landscape stands so clear that one can almost walk into it, into a happy picture of many years ago. I see a teacher with a string of children going out to look at Nature from their meeting place at two o'clock sharp, with no one late, happy, but very orderly. *"Eins, zwei, drei, halt.* Here is a butterfly." "Emil, tell us what you know of butterflies," and on the next day a composition about *"Was wir gestern auf dem Schulausflug beobachtet haben."*

The thought of German children is one to weep over.

The frame of mind that makes things so beautiful always widens into hatred when I think of someone I dislike, for example our Professor of Design who was at the German school in the few miserable years I attended it.

He prided himself upon the faultless discipline in his classroom. No boy ever asked to step out; the hour there, which might have been one of few happy ones, began with the wordless entrance of the pupils, at the minute before the hour, after they had formed themselves into a column of two rows outside the door. We marched in, turned sharply at our assigned benches, and sat down erect, with both hands, palm down, in front of us.

The Professor stepped up to his desk and tapped with a pencil. This meant to put pencil number one, the soft graphite, on the table; the next tap brought pencil number two, the harder; the next tap, the eraser; then the dust cloth, and after that the drawing block. Then he ran around; pencils were held up to show that they were properly sharpened; the Primus of the class was allowed to bring out of a box a wooden sphere for each student to draw.

This evil teacher ruined whatever free talent there was in his class, helped us to hate paper and pencils, and most of all himself and his room and the building he was in.

It is hard when thinking of Germans, without considering the war and other nations but themselves, to rhyme them with themselves.

The dear old ladies that sit in Munich on streetcar crossings and switch the tramways, they have apple faces and alpine hats; the ease and wellbeing in my grandfather's house, he is a Bavarian brewer and loves everybody; the rightness of a simple life; the Sunday promenades with new hats; concerts, and in the evening singing excursions out to a simple tree-shaded summer restaurant. Mild, kind, and good, content with so little and altogether respectful, those of course are the people. The brutality comes from the Uniform, the policeman, the official. I love half of them, the other half I detest.

A Trip to Mississippi

SOME of the men are released from here as cured, others are transferred. One man was released for some reason that no one can understand. He has murdered a man, is degenerate and awful looking. He is not sent home but allowed the freedom of the Hospital, and they have sent him to me for work. I have put him into the kitchen, where he peels potatoes. He has the little knife in his hand, and I am afraid he will use it some day, but it is the only work we can give him. Even the kitchen gang is scared of him and they watch him from the side. He shouted at Mulvey to stop singing, and Mulvey, who would not stop for a sane man twice the size of this patient, was quiet for a long time.

The men who are sent home have in most cases a guard

to take care of them and deliver the patient safely. In this way our men travel all over the country.

There is a considerate arrangement to give all the men trips, and turns are taken. Most men are chosen so that they can take prisoners to places which are their own homes or in the vicinity of the cities from where they come, and in this again is evident the interest in the men and the latitude the Government allows in making the duty of Army life as easy as possible.

Besides, there is great generosity on the part of the Government in conducting these trips. On overnight or very long trips sleepers are provided. Meals may be taken in the dining car, and even short rides are luxurious, in upholstered coaches, not as in Germany, where soldiers travel in the baggage car or in the fourth class, which has benches of wood. Besides that, our pay is good, our meals are fine, we receive ten percent extra because there is a war, besides a few dollars more for this or that, and it is altogether very decent and liberal.

I cannot believe myself to be an American, just because I have a citizen paper, even if I am in the Army, but I could not think of myself as a patriot for any nation. This is interesting to me and I am thankful that there is little or no patriotism among the soldiers. They will fight and even be killed, but they do it, even the crude ones, with the same feeling as if they were repairing a truck and it rolled over them. This seems a bigger field of sentiment and thinking than the Germans are capable of and I think it makes men better soldiers. The Germans are tied up with three little holy grails; they constantly shout and march around with them, and it seems too few to me. Also they are too subordinate and think too little of themselves; they are willing to be kicked as long as there is someone below to whom they can pass that kick.

But this is also wrong because there are magnificent people among them, and I have often set my mind never again to speak or think of nations in the mass. Even if there are only a few among them that are good, it is unfair; and it is fine of the Americans that now, here in the War, they let me speak German, tell me that Germany is beautiful, and don't say a word that I have a stack of German books and many German Ideas. I am truly thankful for all this and respect it. I have often talked to Beardsley of such Ideas, that I do not believe that all men are created equal, and many other things; he calls that "Nickel Philosophy." A Nickel is a five-cent piece in the meaning of this criticism.

On the railroad stations of Buffalo and all other cities are buffets with Red Cross ladies who stuff the soldiers with cookies, chocolate, and candies, also coffee, and one does not have to take a train to get that at any time. They speak a lot and are too sweet, but they mean well and some of them are even young and beautiful.

It is my duty to take a man back home. I think this is because none of our men come from Mississippi and I have told the man who assigns patients that I would like to go anywhere, far away, if possible to the State of Wyoming, Montana, or Colorado, but this trip is to Mississippi.

Mississippi is filled with colored people and so is the patient I am taking there.

This man, the Negro, is a maniac of the violent type. He has not been a soldier, but a civilian employee who was apparently mad when he got into work for the Army. Therefore he is not under the complete protection of the military, but he is a United States Citizen and his part of the country is responsible for him. Although he is not a soldier, he has a Uniform.

My orders are to deliver him to the civil Authorities of Purvis, Mississippi. Nobody here knows where that is, but I have a long ticket—it is about three feet and of many different colors and at the end of the many connected papers is one printed: "From Jackson to Purvis, Mississippi." Ahead of Jackson come many towns; in one, Cincinnati, we have to change trains.

I receive the papers, an order in which my authority and instructions are made clear, a paper which is the receipt from the Government for my patient, and also the instruction to bring the straitjacket back with me.

The red-headed Irishman gives me some advice before I go. I asked if it is possible at times to let the man loose in his straitjacket because the trip is long and his arms in them must become dead, but he forbids this under all circumstances, not even to undo it one notch. Then I see the man; he is very big and already tied up in his jacket. It has a stiff collar and his arms are tightly bound to his sides. He is being fed. The feeding is the same procedure as with all these cases: the attendant takes the man's head in the crook of his elbow and with a spoon goes quickly into his mouth when the patient opens it, which sometimes he must be forced to do. The spoon is then taken out very quickly or he will chew it up and not let go.

I am not very certain now that this will end right. The man is a good deal higher than I and I think much stronger. Even with his arms bound he has the use of his legs and his teeth. But the Irishman says he is stupid, and not to be afraid, and not to let him ever know I am afraid. Besides I want to make this trip very badly. I also have my forty-five Colt with me—the Authorities here know nothing about the experience in Ward Number Three. Here again America is fine. I remember in Germany, in the boarding school, a little boy had done something bad in the first class; his teacher put remarks of this and about his character into the papers and they traveled with him all through his school years, so that every new teacher knew what he was like and he never could enter clean into a new classroom and start with freedom.

The complete authority over another human being such as I have now frightens me. I make up my mind that I will be more than kind to him.

The Ambulance of the Fort Hospital takes us down to the train in Buffalo. I have talked to the patient in quiet words, as the Irishman talks when there are no troubles, but he does not hear or answer me. He rolls his eyes, and I hope, if an attack comes off, it is here in the ambulance where I have trained aid, someone who knows what to do.

As I get him on the train and have both hands busy pushing him up the stairs of the car, a little boy comes and wants to take my gun. His mother just pulls him away; these children need a little order in their lives, I have often observed that.

When we are on the train, the porter says that I cannot go into the sleeper with a colored man, but I explain to him that we must be together and that it is the order of the United States Army. That seems not to impress him, but he looks at our tickets and, because he is a colored man himself, he changes our berth to one close to the door and below one which is not occupied.

After dinner is served for the other passengers, we go into the dining room and order some food for the patient. Then I have to feed him. I have so far hidden his straitjacket under his Army coat, but now I have to put the coat away so that I can hold him. All the waiters in this dining car are colored, and they all stand around while he is fed. He does not look at them or say anything while he eats; only his eyes are like those of a scared horse, and he gets ahold of the tip of the spoon, but I manage to bend it out of his teeth. The waiters are ready to help me; they all look as scared as the patient, and they cannot go away and do their work; they seem very unhappy.

To go to bed is a large problem. The bed is wide enough and I am tired and don't mind sleeping next to the man, but I am afraid he might bite my ears or nose off during the night, and there is also the possibility that he might get loose.

We have some straps that the porter got me and rope and strings; with these I tie my patient loosely to his corner, where the baggage net is. This net comes off and I put it over his head. Then the porter tells me that I can have the vacant upper berth, so I take a long piece of string and bind it around the man's neck and have it run up to my berth, where I attach it to my wrist in case he should break loose. But I cannot sleep and neither can he; therefore I sit up and untie him again and talk with the porter. As to everybody, I have to explain to him why I am in the American Army and not in the German.

The next morning I wash the patient and give him his breakfast; there are some people here in the dining room and again I have to explain the whole business to them and they ask me if I am not afraid. I am no longer, but I was up to now.

We are coming into Cincinnati. At a station just before we

get there, arrives a very elegant young woman, who is smartly dressed, with an intelligent, direct face. Of a very efficient body, she wears a suit of smoky gray with some color, that of eggplants, in its design. This color seems also to be in her eyes.

This young woman comes over to the table after I have fed the patient again and is the first who does not ask questions but talks, and I find out that she has been to Innsbruck. She knows also the cogwheel railroad to Oberbozen, also Munich. Of this city she knows all my favorite streets, the radishwomen, the women who sit in the rain and change the tracks of the streetcar, the little restaurant behind the Frauenkirche, and she has been to the lovely Marionette Theater of Papa Schmidt on the Promenade Platz. She lives in Cincinnati and there is a stop between trains of almost a day before I can go on to Jackson.

In Cincinnati there are again the "Welcome, Boys" signs and the ladies. We get coffee and cake. There is also a large dance that evening at a house of the girl's friends, and she asks me to dinner. There is only the patient, whom I cannot very well bring. He is completely absent in mind and has not said a word all this time. He follows me wherever I go and makes no sign of trouble.

This party seems to be fine. On the station are several more girls; they all have lovely ankles, well ordered hair, and good. clothes. Therefore I have an Idea. I ask a policeman where Headquarters are; then we get one of the girls' cars and drive to this station. It is in a large building in the center of the town up a hill from the depot.

A Lieutenant of Police is at the desk. I ask him if I can leave the patient with him for a day. This is of course an offense, but the man can do no harm with a lot of big police around him, and besides I would mind it only if he were aware of it. In his eyes is nothing, nor in his entire person; he is numb and does not know what goes on around him or where he is, or who he is.

First I have to explain to the Lieutenant and to all the police why I am in the American Army and not the German; then they speak German to me, almost all of them, and finally the Lieutenant says I can leave the patient. It is allright with him and not against regulations, only I have to pay 75 cents for his food and keep. That is allright. They all laugh again because I still have a purse to keep my money in. On it is a picture of Klobenstein in Tirol and under it in golden letters is written: "Greetings from beautiful Klobenstein." Then I am given a receipt, and they take the patient away. This is a guilty thing to do, and I feel as if I were leaving a child alone, but they promise to be nice to him and also not to open the straitjacket. He has eaten and I will feed him when I get back again.

We took a trip up a little mountain in the vicinity of the City. It has a cable car like some mountains in Tirol and on top is a museum. At the entrance of it stand two knights that are copies of the silver knight in the Hofkirche in Innsbruck, and they make me feel very far away. Around this hill is much of Cincinnati's "Beautiful Dreck."

The dinner is very fine, the dance also; everybody in this city seems to be German and at least talk it. They also know Doris and her family in Buffalo. They are brewers, so was my Grandfather a brewer. When we drive back to the station I think of the kitchen gang and how rough they are with their terrible girls, and with this to strengthen me I kiss the girl in

the car, without asking for permission first, and this seems
to be the way to do this, because she allows it and holds still
and only says it's too bad I have to go.

The Lieutenant at Police Headquarters takes me up with
a lift to where the patient has been all this while. He says he
would gladly pay for having him stay.

On one of the upper floors is a large iron construction like
a huge birdcage and in it are lots of people—small crooks
and harlots that have been locked up for minor offenses, also
peddlers and beggars that come here to keep warm.

In this room the police say is a continuous deafening noise
and much cursing, whistling, and booing and many fights,
but not since my patient is here; now it is quiet like in church.

For all the time he has sat on one side of the cage, and
they, all together and close as they can get to each other,
opposite him. They stared at him and he at them. He must
have known that they were afraid because he rolled his eyes
and made faces, also growled. All this time they have been
in terror, and when he moved, sliding a few inches, they
moved a few inches to keep the most distance between him
and themselves.

I have a little more time. My patient is fed, but first we
have to remove his trousers and clean them. This has happened
three times on this trip so far. When they are clean and dried,
we are ready to go. The Lieutenant said: *"Auf Wiedersehen,"*
and gave me back the 75 cents, also some cigarettes, and asked
me to stop any time I came to Cincinnati.

The coach in which we ride next is filled with noises; it
wobbles, and, except for the patient and myself and at times
the conductor, who is not inclined to talk, it is completely
empty.

The train stops frequently. I think it has a woodburning engine because after a stop we always pass a pile of cut timbers. Also there are at times scrubby forests, but they are irregular, not like the deep forests around Munich and in Tirol, where each tree stands behind another one in a straight orderly line and is tall and even. The trees do not look too healthy, and when a patch is passed, there comes again a wide stretch of red land. It lies in waves like the sea in a wind that is not yet a storm.

Over this landscape the sun sets redder than I have ever seen it and also twice the size it is in Buffalo. Far apart are houses, shacks of unpainted wood. For some reason the fallen apart ones do not look half as unhappy as the ones that are lived in, with smoke coming out of them. That is because I feel lonesome for whoever has not moved away from there. This scene is again like a melody, of violins that play on deep strings. The man without mind that is my patient is in his bundle so good and quiet, so sad and lost, it seems it would be kindest to shoot him rather this minute than the next and bury him in his land here, so that he could find release and go back to the earth.

There are no civil Authorities in Purvis, Mississippi. There is a sawmill and one street with chickens in it and two pigs. On both sides of it are filthy houses and sunflowers. In the houses that are covered with the red mud and are open to the four winds, people, all colored, animals, and many children live together.

After looking very close and long at him, they recognize the patient or admit he is one of them. He was well when he left them; now he is back, he recognizes no one. The people take me to one house; in there is his family. One woman shrieks and weeps, the children stare, and the men look at me with anger.

I tell them that he will be better, that this takes time, and that after a while the straitjacket can be taken off him and then he will be as happy as he was before. They weep and look angry and I wonder what to do. I cannot leave him here; my orders are to the civil Authorities of Purvis. Where are they?

The Authorities arrive, in the shape of a man with a dirty white suit and a sharp thin face. He has two horses with him and is some kind of mayor and gendarme. He also knows this man and of me bringing him here.

Over night he will take care to have him in a lockup and then take him away tomorrow on the next train. The little train on which I have come will be back again; it runs one day to the south, the next to the north, and stops one day altogether. I must go back with this train. First we bring the patient to the lockup. Somebody will stay with him through the night, and in the morning I will feed him and show this man how this is done. We also have to take care of his trousers again. His wife is going to wash them, and in the meantime he has others to wear. Then we ride away.

This Authority has a big house behind several hills. It has thick-leaved exotic trees and plants and is weathered but of fine classic design, with columns, one of which is missing. I get a room, the biggest I have ever slept in, on one of the upper floors.

In the morning we have a rich breakfast of fried chicken with sweet sauce and very fine coffee, then I get a receipt of the Authority for the patient, and also give him the papers.

As it is time for the train, we ride down to the lockup. My patient sits there in the morning sun, outside with somebody

that is nice and kind, and I think, if anywhere, in this landscape that he must love as I do Tirol, he might get well. Three
strong men are around him and they are his friends.

Now I have to get the straitjacket. I said to the man in
Authority: "You take it off," but he says: "Oh, no, and you
are not going to take it off him either." Then the train whistles;
we have to hurry because I cannot stay here for three days.

In Buffalo the straitjacket is taken out of my pay; it cost
$13.50.

Leave of Absence

EVERYBODY can have a leave of absence in the American Army, if he asks for it. Some men don't ask and just go away, which in wartime is desertion in any other Army and punishable by death.

Here it is different. If he is gone, they wait if he will not come back himself within the short while of a few weeks; if he comes back himself, little happens to him, at the most a few days in the Guardhouse or he is docked his pay or demoted if he has any rank; after six more weeks he is officially absent without leave, then when he comes back himself he still is not severely punished, but he is courtmartialed and goes to the Guardhouse for several weeks; only after a long while,

113

I think it is six months, does he become an official deserter, and they start looking for him.

We are given frequent leaves of absence because of the nature of the Hospital. I have saved up my allowance to be able to go to New York. Why I want to go there I don't know, except that, since I landed there and lived in that city first, I have been thinking of it as my home in America, and I think it is the Idea of going home, that everybody else speaks of so much, that I feel I need. Besides, I get transportation if I take a patient along, and I have also some money. We are well paid and cannot spend any money, at least not much, because we are always invited. There are very few soldiers in Buffalo and many patriotic ladies who need them for their entertainments.

The house in which I lived in New York belongs to a lovely old lady, German, with a daughter who is very young and pretty. Her name is Ada Bach. The house is away from New York, near the Botanical Gardens and a park. It is reached with the subway and a streetcar; it is old and roomy and peculiar; it was the mansion in an estate. Trees stand around it, and in front is a lawn out of which stick a few rocks. There is a hill to the right, no other houses around, and a vegetable garden in back. I lived here chiefly because I could take my dog for runs in the country and because it was quiet.

Ada sometimes writes to me; I have been thinking much of that house and my room and of Ada, and lately I have thought and pictured how I will try and see if I can make love to her.

The nightly talk of the soldiers in their beds made me of the opinion that the way Mulvey and the kitchen gang do it is the best way, that is, without much ceremony, a few words and gestures, but complete indifference and confidence, as if it were accomplished before one starts. I know the formula by heart, it is simple and does not ask for much effort or imagination. It either works or one knows soon that it doesn't.

After I delivered my patient in New York, I took the subway home, and near the park I had to change to the streetcar. This streetcar passes a riding academy, and I got off to hire a horse to start things right. It is a short ride, and Ada was home, and I managed to ride in and be very much admired. I tied the horse to a tree and we had dinner. Mrs. Bach had cooked something very fine, Ada had on a lovely dress and kissed me, and so far it was very successful. Only during dinner Mrs. Bach asked whether I rode the horse all the way from Buffalo.

Afterwards I had to take the horse back, and it was soon evening. Many relatives came and nothing happened, except that I thought everything would be allright by my first of all being very certain of success. There was one difficulty—Mrs. Bach and Ada sleep in the same bed and in the same room— so I had to think of something different.

The next morning is Saturday and Ada asks me to go to the City with her. We ride in the subway, arm in arm, and everybody smiles stupidly at us. We ride very far downtown. She wants me to see her Office and her boss.

This man is a lawyer by the name of Mirror, and he says we must come to dinner at his house that evening.

In the Office I am introduced to another girl and a young man. Ada sits down at the typewriter and writes, and smiles at me to show me how well she can write without looking at the machine, and also chews gum at the same time. The other girl is allowed to see all this and I get a chair. Ada can go early and Mr. Mirror calls up his house and tells his wife that we, Ada and I, are coming with him to dinner that evening.

The house in which he lives is on East 193rd Street; it is called Oxford Hall. Towards the street it has a very imposing façade; around it, two feet away from the building on the sidewalk and sunk into thick concrete posts, are swollen brass pipes. A court opens into the building from the street; in its center is a cement fountain, and left and right of the door are two cement lines.

In an outer hall are rows and rows of names, and the one we look for is written out: "Stanley B. Mirror, Councillor at Law."

The upper part of the foyer is decorated as if someone had smeared an unthinkable material with his five fingers on the wall; up to the chest it is of white marble. In the middle stands a gold painted elevator shaft. A boy in uniform with "Oxford Hall" written on him is inside of it when the elevator comes down.

He takes us up and there is a long corridor. All the way up in all these corridors I see baby carriages; there are four on this, the top floor.

I would like to run away because I am certain I don't like this, but it is too late. At the door is a card, again with "Stanley B. Mirror, Councillor at Law," written on it. The door opens and we step into a long narrow hall at the end of which is the dining room.

The furniture in this room is of a period called Mission; it is so big and the room so very little that we all sit glued to the table. Mr. Mirror is a little man, the table is high, the side-board is close behind him, and the grapefruit on the table is almost in his nose. His face has no more identity than the grapefruit. It is decorated with thickly rimmed glasses and a small mustache, but that only makes it more like all such faces that I have seen everywhere in New York.

They are good people and it is unkind to not be grateful and polite to them, but I feel a strong repulsion in me, against all this, the house, the furniture, Mr. Mirror, and I would like to get up and tell them that I do not like it and go away. But this is of course impossible.

Mrs. Mirror also has glasses, thin ones with a little chain; she is a woman who is not a mother, not a girl, not a mistress or wife type. She is ordinary, unlovely, and only female in an unhappy sense. Her flesh is white, bloated, and porous; she must be hideous in the bath; her voice is metallic and too big for the room, and her hands are common.

The conversation is mostly of Mr. Mirror's making; he had an argument with the superintendent of the building in the morning, and while he eats he tells how he told that man to see that there was enough hot water or some such business, also about a radiator. He insists on being heard. He says over and over again: "Listen to me, listen to me," at any time when everybody's attention is not his. If that doesn't help, he takes hold of his wife's arm or my sleeve and pulls. He starts every sentence like this, three times mostly: "Then I said to him, then I said to him, listen to me, then I said to him, you know what I told him?"

At one time I turned around to look out of the window, which was behind my chair. Outside was a suicidal picture, millions of bricks, run this way and that and up and down, and they became narrow lines far below; they ended on a metal roof with a skylight; rows of windows were along the shaft. When I looked back in the room he still went on: "He always gives me an argument, that guy." For the rest the conversation here is as if it were written on building blocks that are thrown from one person to another; nothing is ever said.

Ada seems to be at home here; she can join in and say the things to which they answer easily and in which they are versed and secure. Sitting next to me; she eats with one hand. So must I because she has my hand in hers, except when she cuts a piece of chicken. Whenever anything comes to the table she says: "Oh, its so delicious." In saying this she pauses at the letter L, leaving her tongue against the upper teeth for a moment too long. It sounds: "Dee - llicious." She does the same with "Beautifu - ll" and to the icecream she said:

"Oh, I think it's the most dee - llicious thing I ever put in my mouth."

But that is not all; they wish to come tomorrow and visit Mrs. Bach's house. Ada says they will be delighted, and I can't very well say otherwise. Mr. Mirror will bring his camera and take pictures of us, and afterwards we will go to the Botanical Gardens and after that to a movie on 168th Street.

Ada says once more that everything was "so dee - llicious." We leave the house and I am glad of the fresh air after we get out of the golden elevator.

We took a taxi. It was not far from home, and since I no longer wanted it, I could have my way on this first evening. Just to try out their value, I used one of Mulvey's phrases and gestures; she seemed to know it, followed in words and motion, and seemed willing to comply.

But all desire was gone.

The typewriter which she can work without looking at it, Oxford Hall, and Mrs. Mirror have done it. Now there is a relaxed dumbness in her face. She is a sweet-smelling animal without will. The lower lip hangs loose, the line of her neck is clumsy, the ankles are too thick, but my dislike fastens itself chiefly on the "Dee - llicious."

I try to think of Mulvey's terrible girls—they are so much worse than Ada—but that is better, they are at least strong— and I also say to myself: Why be so very choosing, after all it is not a pleasure of the mind. But it is.

in Mr. Shillings House

The Widow from Scranton

FRAU BACH has a brother, and he has a son who is a riveter in the Navy Yard, but is not a sailor. He lives at our house and has a little car. I know his father, who was a barber and is an old gentleman, little, fat, with very light blue eyes. The father's name is Lorenz Schilling and the son's Eddy.

It is perhaps from working with a riveting gun that Eddy has a strange way of speaking. He chops the air in a quick move of his right hand, which travels back and forth at the height of his chest the moment he starts saying anything. If he is mad or intent, which often happens, then the chops are shorter and faster. He does that even when we drive, holding the steering wheel with his left hand while with the right he upsets the air. He calls me "Ludy" and he always seems to be

121

mad. Just now he has a piece of steel in his right eye; he says that happens all the time and that they are going to pull it out with a magnet, and then he gets a fortnight off and will take me along up to their farm in Pennsylvania. Mr. Schilling has a frugal chicken farm near a place called Mayfield.

When the steel was removed, we drove up. It was very cold, but Eddy is a tough hard person. When we had to leave a good highway and turn into sideroads that lead to his father's house, he lost the contour of the road, in a place where the wind had evened out the snow. Eddy got out and with his bare hands and without gloves shoveled the snow away, and we both pushed the car a little and it was on the road again. He never said a word until he was in the car; his fingers did not seem to be cold, because he kept on talking and chopping the air again as he had done all the way up. He has mostly talked about a woman with two children, a widow, who lived in a house which he pointed out to me along the road and has since moved to Scranton, but sometimes in the summer comes back here. He has been in love with her and when he speaks of her he says either "the widow," or "the widow from Scranton." It's a very long story and he has repeated the details of it several times.

Mr. Schilling could see us far away because there is nothing around his house except a long chicken barn and a few lilac bushes. The landscape is very beautiful; the property is on a high plateau, and around it in a ring and far away are hills that seem almost mountains.

It's a little warm and friendly house. It has thin walls, and the oven must be kept going all day and night. The windows are clean, with white curtains. In the kitchen at a window is the barber chair and on the sill bottles of different tonics, brushes, and combs.

The first thing Mr. Schilling wants to do is cut my hair; he cannot shave me yet, as I have no beard. He makes a joke about this: he says I have to rub chicken manure and chocolate on my upper lip, the chicken manure inside, the chocolate outside, one pulls and the other pushes. He laughs very long at this joke and then he cuts my hair. He tells me some of the great people whose hair he has cut, and he is very proud of his work.

Mrs. Schilling is a silent wife, but with a shrill voice, worried. Her eyes wander around from the oven to the little pantry. She has asked Eddy five times to get some water outside while I am in the barber chair. He says: "Ah, get it yourself," but finally, when he is through reading, he takes the pail and goes out.

Eddy also has a dog here, a sad, loose animal, a setter. Its name is Girlie, and this dog slips up on him like a rug and tries to cover him all over, and while doing this moans with affection and licks his face. After much wiggling—the dog is very big—it finally succeeds in sitting on Eddy with its head over his face. I can see this in a mirror and the dog moans more, like someone with a heavy weight on him.

Down in the cellar are rows of preserves that Mrs. Schilling makes in the summer—pickles, tomatoes, chopped up sour things, pears, and apples—rows on rows of this—and in a corner coal and firewood and three barrels of a terrible drink called "elderberry wine." It is sweet-sour and contracts the lips so one cannot whistle, and I was given a big glass of it when I came in. It gets dark early, and we have a very good dinner and fine *Apfelstrudel* afterwards, also a cigar for me, and Mr. Schilling goes down for another bottle of the sour elderberry wine. He is going to brew some beer next week.

In the living room is some furniture of a kind that seems to be cut out with a jigsaw, and the grain of the wood is polished up in some varnish that is very bad in color and looks like dark mustard.

After dinner—and Mrs. Schilling has brought everything to the table and sat with us but said nothing—Mr. Schilling goes over to his easy chair. It is a curious piece of machinery; he bought it out of a catalogue and loves it very much. It has a lever on the side, and when one sits in it and pulls that lever, it folds back like an operating table; and when it is that way, Mr. Schilling talks up to the ceiling. The moment he was in this chair, Girlie jumped up, and he scratched the dog behind the ears and talked about his military service.

He did his service in Dresden and is also very fond of the King of Saxony. He speaks, as if praying, of the Kaiser who rode past him in a review. Then he pulls the lever, the dog jumps away, and the chair falls into another shape with a loud bang and stands him up. This is very funny, and to show me how it works, Mr. Schilling sits down again, pulls, and is laid flat. Before Girlie can jump, bang, he stands on his feet again. Then I have to try it, and after this Mr. Schilling walks over to a closet and takes out a broom. To show me that he has not forgotten the manual of arms, he commands himself: "Present arms! Right shoulder arms! Left shoulder arms!" and when he is through with this, he dismisses himself and puts the broom away.

In this room, on the wall, over the mechanical easy chair, hangs a picture of Heidelberg. It is a paper calendar with a pocket under it on which is written the advertisement of the firm that gave them away. A castle is pressed out into relief and is covered with a glassdust, the color of Lifebuoy soap; around the castle is foliage.

In the middle of the room, over the table, hangs a petroleum lamp. Mr. Schilling turns the light down low. The lamp has one of those artless glass shades that are found on drug store counters; they are inlaid with many colors. He turns the shade until a red glass is in the light, and now the castle sparkles as it did when it was festively illuminated for patriotic purposes. Then Herr Schilling sings *"Deutschland, Deutschland, über alles,"* and *"Röslein auf der Heide,"* and winds up an old gramophone with a scratchy record that plays: "Must I leave, must I leave my little city?" While this music is playing, he fills my glass and his own with elderberry wine. "Bottoms up," he says and drinks it down with me, after looking into my eyes and clinking glasses as the code requires.

The music plays and he looks on and on at his castle until two tears run down his lovely face. He does not wipe them away, and I have to go out of the room because it is so sad and lonely.

Eddy had been reading a Western story all the time, with his dog moaning and sitting on him, out in the kitchen, and his mother has washed and dried the dishes and is now looking through eggs and wrapping them.

When it was time to go to bed, we walked upstairs into a room with a slanting floor, a low ceiling, and two iron beds. It was icy here, the beds moist and cold. I had many covers and Eddy went to bed with his warm underwear on although he seems to be so tough. The moon was full and shining into the room, and in its light it was colder still.

I could not sleep and neither could Eddy, and we talked. In a short while Eddy sat up and started again with his widow all over at the beginning, which I knew so well. He has difficulty in telling how very beautiful she was because he knows only a few words or does not wish to use the right ones.

He described the size of her eyes by making a circle with his index finger and thumb and the firmness of her bosoms by making both his open palms tremble about a foot in front of him.

He also told how frequently and well he made love with her, and he said that with Army words. He was with her every day and sometimes all of the night, sometimes from Friday to Monday, and one day she asked him to give her some money to have her hair done in Scranton, in a beauty parlor.

" 'I like you the way you are,' I told her," said Eddy and chopped the air again, "but she wanted ten dollars, see?

"So I give her ten bucks and she goes to Scranton to have her hair fixed.

"When she comes back, she says to me: 'Eddy, how do you like me this way, how do I look?'

" 'You look like Hell,' I says."

He says this with his lips drawn back, tearing the words sharply with his tongue and teeth, and he likes it so much that he repeats: " 'You look like Hell,' I says to her.

"But, Ludy," he continued in soft tones, "she was a pippin, beautiful like nothing you ever laid eyes on, with her hair done up in curls."

Eddy showed the curliness of her hair with his hands as if he were tickling the back of someone in front of himself.

Well then, Eddy had to go away on some work for several

months, and while he was away, a man who had been hanging around the widow for years with serious intentions and
whom Eddy did not like and who also had a farm, some money,
and wanted to take the children and also marry her, which
Eddy did not want to do, became her friend. He became so
bold because Eddy was away and also because the widow was
now so beautiful with her big eyes and the curls.

Eddy in the meantime had saved his money and worked
very hard and he had bought himself a new suit, shoes, hat,
and necktie, and when he came back, the people told him
about the widow and the other man. Eddy wanted to go right
over and beat him and the widow up, but then he thought
differently about it. She was not worth it, no woman is, he
told me, and he stayed home. But he planned his revenge.

On the way up here, whenever Eddy came to this part of
the story, he would drive to the side of the road and stop
the car. Now he got out of bed, and went on.

There was a dance in the next village, to which he knew the
widow and this man would go. It was called a "Social," to cele-
brate the Fourth of July.

And Eddy, dressed in collar and necktie and the new suit
with the straw hat, went to the Social.

Eddy was very worried that I might not have a clear picture of this. He showed me the suit hanging under a curtain
and described at length the hall in which this party took place,
how it was decorated, with flags and streamers and balloons,
and how it was illuminated, and how everybody was there,
with music and refreshments, all the people in the neighbor-
hood sitting around the room along the wall on benches. To
show this, he runs around the little room on the sides of his

feet, because the floor is very cold. "Here was the orchestra, there was the door, and along the wall the people, all the people. Do you get it, Ludy?"

He waited until the party was well under way and then walked in with his new suit. The music stopped and everybody wondered what would happen. The widow laughed like this: "Haha," and walked over to him.

" 'Hello, Eddy,' she says to me, like as if nothing happened. 'Hello, Eddy.'

"Now, Ludy," he went on, "here I was, in the middle of the room with everybody looking, and she was there beautiful like anything with my curls that I paid for. I would have bust him in the jaw right there, but he didn't come out. He sat in the back and looked dumb like.

" 'Hello, Eddy,' she says to me.

" 'Lady,' I says, without even looking at her but so everybody in the room can hear it, 'Lady, you are talking to a man what don't know you,' and I walked out. I didn't even take my hat off."

Then he went to bed. "Tomorrow, Ludy, I'll get you fixed. Got any money? I know some swell dames. You tell Ma you got to go back."

Foyer Polish Kate's

Polish Kate's

THE next day after breakfast we go over to the barn to inspect the chickens. While Mr. Schilling goes inside, Eddy shows me a torn rubber boot in which he has hidden a pint of whisky. He winks and says: "For tonight. You'll be surprised, Ludy!"

The landscape in the morning light is lovely, the air is biting and clear, the horizon wider than yesterday. All objects, even the faraway ones, stand out in clear line and strongest

129

color, almost as if looked at through the sharp lenses of a fieldglass. Girlie is joyful at the still new return of Eddy and gallops through the snow with foolishness and suddenly stops with all four paws outstretched, takes a mouthful of snow, and eats it with joy as if it were icecream. But country is not country without a horse.

Of course Mr. Schilling is glad he can have the chickens, the dog, and his food in order and paid for. His is not an easy life, I think. Feed for the fowls is high, he does not get much for eggs, must clean, grade, and pack them, and the farmers around have their hair cut only once in six months.

Mrs. Schilling comes out of her house, then goes in again; she works without ever halting and since I have been here she has not spoken more than the greetings when I came, yes and no, good night, good morning, and the five-times repeated: "Get me some water, Eddy." She seems not unhappy and is just made the way she is.

Eddy has told me that he knows a house, down in the coal region, where women are kept, he says the most beautiful girls in the world, more beautiful than the widow even. But I am afraid all women are alike to Eddy, because again these girls have the eyes which he described last night as belonging to the widow and also the bosoms two feet in front of him, but we will see. In the meantime it is very exciting to wait for this.

When the light changes, we say good-by and drive off. The car is open; for a while it is bitter cold and we have to drive a long time. And then appears the most beautiful "Dreck" I have ever seen. The snow is smudged; little houses are unbelievably dirty but with much character and warmth; in small towns rise the steeples of Russian churches with onion tops; and behind all this are mountains of black coal with blue lights playing on them. The shapes of crushers rise as high as the towers of Neuschwanstein and much more forbidding; beside the road flows a river, also black. It is as if all the colors had run out of this corner, except a rusty red, black, and indigo. Wherever there is a poster, a lamp, a firebox, it sings out its color and makes the black blacker.

Then we drive up a hill into a town, over railroad tracks. As sad as the moan of Eddy's dog is the sound in the night of the bell on American locomotives. It is like a pulse beat of loneliness, but how beautiful are the engines below! The signal lights have the electric color of Christmas tree glass ornaments, the rails are silver; and the swinging lanterns, the voices of men who shout at each other—all this belongs rightly in this picture.

Past the bridge, a little higher up, we turn past a gas station, and drive into an alley where Eddy leaves the car. He has been quiet all the way down. He says we need one dollar each, and that he has a girl in mind for me, not his kind, he says, but just right for me.

We come to a house in a narrow alley in which all houses are such as the one we enter.

Eddy is known here. The girls—there are two in a little room in front that looks out on the alley—put their arms around him and lean on him, and he is very proud of this ease and welcome. He pats them on the backside, and says to me: "Have I been lying, Ludy?" He hasn't; the light here is dim, but the girls are young, have smooth limbs, firm bosoms, and big eyes. It happens hereabouts that Polish men marry Irish women and from them come children that are pale skinned and very beautiful.

Eddy goes downstairs and says he will be right back; he is

going to see if Julie is in, that is the girl he has for me. But she is out, and the two girls in the hall say: "Why don't you take either of us, at least until she comes back?" But Eddy comes up through the door and on his hand is another woman and he says: "No-o-o—you don't know what's coming, you sit here and wait, Ludy." The woman with him is again beautiful, really so—she is obviously mostly Slavic with a soft rich body, not one that would look well in clothes on the street, but so generous and warm that it makes the blood hammer at my temples; her lips are moist, the eyes black, black, her skin clear and white. Eddy slaps her on the wide haunches, and they walk up a narrow stair.

"You wait there until she comes and don't give her more than I told you," says Eddy and disappears with his woman.

There is a foolish little sofa with a summer slip cover on it in the entrance hall where I am sitting. On the right of it, and so hot that one can only sit on the far end of this couch, is an iron stove, small with a round belly and heated to glowing in the most beautiful color. This room is about ten by eleven feet, but the heat goes up mostly. In front of the stove are the two girls. They lean out into a box that is built into the window out on the street, so they can look up and down. When a man passes, they play a small pantomime and knock and then wipe the film of vapor from the pane so they can see again. From where I sit I can see them; they have bare legs in mules, two loose robes as if in a bath house draped around them. They lean over forward with their legs wide apart, and in this position is much sensuality. It also portrays how much they love the warmth of the oven in back of themselves.

From below comes a mixture of voices and the cry of a baby.

There is a wallpaper in this room that I will never forget, just as anything I will see and feel in this house will always be with me. I have never been so beautifully nervous on any day of my life, and I have lost the sense of guilt which I felt walking up to this house.

Then Julie comes in from the dark street; she is again what Eddy promised, not more beautiful than the others, who are lovely in the manner of peasant girls. She has slim heels and a finer face. I do not know the rules of behavior here, whether I am to introduce myself and how to ask her, but that is all done for me. One of the girls says: "He wants you," and she says without looking: "Just a minute," and disappears downstairs.

She had a raincoat buttoned high with a belt in the center, ashen hair, and a hat like a southwester that sailors have. When she returns she has a long simple emerald-colored dress with a small ornament that catches the folds of the dress in the center of her loins. The dress is exquisite in cut and I wonder how it can be bought by girls who cannot have much money. Besides, it is in best taste.

"Come on," she says; she has a strange voice, and I wonder whether there is a spell in this house that all things seem so wondrously beautiful.

The upper part of this house is divided into compartments, many of them with thin walls. We come to one in which Julie turns on the light. She holds out her hand first of all. "Give me the money," she says. I give it to her, more; because one dollar seems disgraceful. "I'll get you change afterward," she says.

In this partition of the house is a bed. It has a mattress without a cover and a pillow covered with waxcloth. There is a chair, a bureau with a stack of towels on it, about twenty of them; on the chair is a basin; a stout colored woman comes in and fills the basin with water. There is also a little glass jar with some disinfectant in it and from this the room smells of carboleum.

On the floor are six different kinds of linoleum, small pieces put together like in a game; pasted on the wall are pictures of John Barrymore, Jack Holt, William Farnum, Pauline Frederick, Norma Talmadge, Mary Pickford, and Theda Bara. They are cut out of rotogravure sections, and their cheeks and lips are colored with rouge. From the ceiling hangs a naked electric light bulb on a black wire, and a piece of black electrician's tape along the bulb.

It is obvious for what reason I came here, but again I feel like a child. What is the next thing to do? I must look at her; even in this unkind light she is so beautiful. I sit down at the bed; she lies down next to me and folds her arms under her head, and then I do the same. Afterwards I turn my face and look at her and she turns her face and looks quietly, with her eyes looking at my mouth. Outside are the coal hills, the ring of the train bell, and there must be a stable in back of the house because I can hear the sound of horses when they change their positions. The ceiling of the room at which I look is painted blue, a light color with much white in it, most probably a bad job by anybody around the house, but because of that it has the marks of the brush and is nice.

My long problem with life on earth is here again. I think that it is not like Schopenhauer says; I think that in this life we have few and far apart completely wonderful happinesses. Here and now is one such moment, in which all things are right, even the six pieces of linoleum on the floor, the coal hills outside, and the bells—who would ever come here to find it?

Such moments come not only in love. I have felt them at concerts, mostly when the orchestra, after its fullest playing, leaves a space of silence between the pulses of the kettledrums, the pause between the dull thuds half a second apart of two soft "booms" on the copper drums, which often happens in Wagner music and is filled with melody although there is not a sound. The quiet pauses between words, here with Julie, were like that.

Through the thin wall next door come voices; there are another man and a woman, and some of the talk is silent, but when they speak loud it is again in words that belong so well in this house. The woman talks most of the time; she is apparently jealous of some other woman, and the pieces of talk go like this:

"He knows I'm sitting here boiling."
"Let's not spoil the whole thing, I said to him.
It's the thing that counts."
"You're up against a stone wall, I said to him.
You know what a stone wall is."
"It's not fair for a guy like that to go to a girl that's been brought up in the church and say: Who is God? How do you know it's true? A guy like him, that's been practicing atheism for years."
"Well, honey, you wanted Steve, here's Steve.
I'm on my way, I told her."
"I thought she'd soften up, women like her soften up sometimes. But not that one."
"Allright, I said, if you don't believe me, maybe you'll

believe my lawyer. Oh, gee, Joe, don't laugh. It ain't funny a bit, not for me it isn't."

All this time, Julie has been looking at me and at the loud parts of the lament next door, making grimaces of sorrow, amusement, and mock anger. "This goes on all the time," she said. She has been holding my hand all the while and abruptly she says: "Do something for me, will you?" And when I ask her what, she says: "Kiss me, I never kiss anyone."

Her body is young and firm; her back with the contour of the spine, the shoulder blades, and the pelvis of finest modeling; her abdomen, the armpits, the inside of the elbows, soft and without fault. I have always thought that such a life would waste all beauty.

"Why don't you put a shade on that lamp?" I asked her, as if I had known her all my life.

"The chiselers would take it right along, they take everything when they're drunk. We had a beautiful standing lamp down in the hall, a guy walked right out with it the first night. There was a kid here, a week ago, he didn't like the light either. He took his socks off, blue they were, and pulled one over the light, but it got hot and went on fire. The time we had! The room was full of smoke."

We had to laugh at this.

"Look what I can do," said Julie and stood on her head in the bed.

"Why do you do that?" I asked.

"Oh, I don't know," she said. "Just for fun. And look"—she pointed at her toes and spread them like two fans.

And after this I have to sit up and laugh, and nothing can happen. It is strange that this business of love demands solemnity, one cannot do anything with it laughing. It has, I think, something to do with breathing or nerves; it needs absolute concentration. Ever since Julie has been funny and wiggled her toes, everything is impossible.

She buttons me up and kisses me again. "Here's your money," she said and pushed it into my pocket. "Come down with me. I'll make you some coffee."

There is a bent and twisted stairway down the back of the house, and in the basement is a room with an oven in it and in a crib a little baby that belongs to the stout colored cleanup woman. Two girls sit and look at it and point their lips and follow its eyes with their faces. It is very, very young, with fingernails the size of a grain of rice. Over the tiny face wander trembling changes—a wide grin from ear to ear, then, with great effort and clenched fists, the face of scorn and suspicion. The little pale eyes wander in a wide arc and try to look around two corners; when it has done this, after an undecided pause, the lower lip quivers and falls away in a bitter helpless cry. It was well comforted; one of the women carried it back and forth, the other walked along, up and down, and spoke to it softly.

There is also a man with his hat on and a wardrobe trunk full of exquisite evening dresses. They come from New York, from debutantes and society women. He tells with each dress the name of the lady who owned it, and of course each name is one that everybody knows. Now I know where the lovely emerald one comes from.

Eddy comes down and asks me how it was. He has to go home to the farm, and I am going to get a room at the Y.M.C.A. and take a train the next day to New York.

In back of the house is a stable in which the old horse made the bumpy drum noises as it changed its position. I go in to him; his stable smells sweet, and the horse is plain and strong with flaxen hair. I have an excuse to go back to the house for sugar. I want to hear her voice once more, to see if she is so lovely, if her hair and her eyes are what I saw before. She is all that.

The Hospital in FORT PORTER BUFFALO

The Army Is Like a Mother

THE Army is like a mother; one cannot go hungry or without a bed. It is my home. I like the patients and love some of
them; in their illness they are so alone, and the madness, even
when it is dangerous or unfortunately amusing, calls from me
not pity but some kind of respect. They seem more grave and
interesting, stronger; they appear to me like actors with half
their make-up on.

The Army issues a book of a few pages in which almost all
things are taken care of. Punishment and reward, advice and
consequences, are written into sober paragraphs for the guid-
ance of the men. The spirit of this book is clearest in the advice
given to non-commissioned Officers on how to make men who
have quarreled friends again. On this problem the book states

139

that the men are to be put to the duty of washing windows, one outside, the other inside, washing the same pane. Looking at each other they soon have to laugh and all is forgotten; they push up half of the window and shake hands. It works, I have tried it. Soldiers are terribly childish and forgive easily because they have no rent, wife, insurance, etc., to worry them down.

On the train back to Buffalo I have many hours to think over the last days. Whenever I think of Julie, I feel as if I were back in the young days of my childhood, standing on my toes with arms back and face up, breathing deeply and singing, or looking into the clouds, without a wish other than that this happiness might last forever.

Beardsley told me once that "our dubious Society, and mostly that in the West," was mothered by women out of such houses. The hard men that went out to settle the wild lands married them chiefly for the reason that women were then very scarce out there and even back here.

I can understand that and like it, even without the reason of scarcity. Immoral seem to me the breed of women like Mrs. Mirror and undesirable girls like Ada. I have often seen open enmity and disgust in the faces of married people. I have seen so very seldom an unreserved frank admission in their eyes that they are glad of each other or even interested.

In the subway in New York I also remember the dreadful deadness and stare and the inner upset and drive that is clearly written in the way they sit and move their lips silently, or look constantly as if they have forgotten something and were trying to remember where it was. Free of this seem only sailors, soldiers, some policemen, and most Negroes. They have privacy and seem not to care about much.

Another thing I wondered about is how much they dislike

any person that seems not to be like themselves. In one train
a man came in and sat down; he had a funny hat on and gaiters
on his shoes, also a collar that was not the kind anybody wears—
it stuck over his chin left and right. He read a little book and
blew his nose on a large blue handkerchief. The people who
lined the seats along both walls watched him with displeasure
from the moment he came in; their eyes all swam over to his
shoes and up and down him as if he had stolen from them. I
wished he would take a big gun out of his pocket and scare
them to death.

On the train up I also have imperial Ideas again. I think
that America needs someone like our King Ludwig, who was
a little mad, but made his country beautiful. Someone who has
arrogant power and says: "I want a wide avenue through the
City of New York, three times as wide as Fifth Avenue, with
light, monuments, fountains, and parks!" who gets the finest
artist, not one who ruins the scenery with bad work, but the
best, no matter whether he be in Paris or anywhere.

"Make the Hudson beautiful from the Palisades down,
forbid such houses as Oxford Hall, and do away with the
Jersey Meadows!" The Hudson is much more majestic than
the Rhine. It is not always so beautiful, for the Rhine is lovely
in the Spring because of the many trees in blossom that go
down to the banks and also because it winds much more and,
of course, the castles and ruins are nicer than the factories.

All things that are for utility need not be ugly, and it can
only be done with great and absolute power. Some people
might lose something for a while, although there is no need
even for that, but in the end New York and America could be
the most beautiful and proudest land in the world.

But I fear this is a leftover of my German heritage and

training, the wish to settle everything and have absolute order. Perhaps Mr. and Mrs. Mirror are happy and should be left alone in Oxford Hall, and so with everybody else. That is, I think, Democracy, and besides I have found that Beautiful Dreck is really very fine. Think of Scranton and the trains racing through the Jersey marshes, also the colored flames, the smoke from the lighting plants there, and the mist on the ground. It's just as well to leave it as it is.

In New York two detectives have brought a man on the train between them; he was handcuffed and looked somewhat like Mulvey. I no longer dislike Mulvey and his gang; they are rough but, I think, out of having been made so, and I also think in their way they are honest. I am glad to go back to the Hospital again.

I am most happy to go back to the friendship of the little Chaplain. I can see his gait always. He is so young that I can never get myself to call him father and always get around it by saying either nothing or "you"; I cannot very well call him Philip yet. He is so young that he whips on his toes as he walks along, a very gentle motion one sees in boys. They step as he does, touching the ground first with the front of the shoe, then with energy lifting the palm of the foot, and then the heel goes down. That walk is much of his person. I imitated him on a little walk and he blushed and smiled. He is altogether good and fine, but he will not like my ideas on Morality and it will be best not to upset him with Polish Kate's house.

Barracks Bayonet School

Bayonet School

THE Army needs Officers very badly, and a general order has been issued from Washington to the effect that each post can send one out of a given number of enlisted men to Officers' Training Camp. A board of Officers here gave me a very kind examination; I also passed the physical test—all through my good friend the young priest—and then I received transportation and orders to report to the command at the Officers' Training School at Camp Gordon, which is near Atlanta, Georgia.

Here blows a different wind. The day is cut up into minutes, and from the early morning to the hour of retreat almost every step is counted. It is almost German. In a short period they must make Officers out of civilians and get as much West Point training into them as possible.

To every eight men a young Officer is assigned. He is like a governess, but a strict one. He has a little book with the names of his men in it—we are called candidates—and he watches us all day. These men, who are Second Lieutenants, are somewhat arrogant, and the only consolation is that in a short while we can hand it on to the next group.

Demerits are called "skins." A button undone, a book on the shelf over the bed out of alignment, a shoe under the bed not laced up (even without the foot in it), or looking down when marching at attention to the faraway drill grounds—any of these things means a skin. Sixty of them is the limit during the training. One more, and the Benzine Board, as they call the Faculty, takes prompt action and throws the candidate back into a Sergeant's Uniform.

I get by and go to the Bayonet School; a berth here is very much envied because we can wear spurs, although we have no horses. Not much happens that is funny, because the work is very exacting, leaving no time for jokes. I have gained weight, feel wonderful, and my only sorrow is that when I drill the men, they sometimes have to laugh. I can shout: "At hease!" so it flies across a whole battalion clear and right. We have practiced this in the woods, shouting commands for days, but I have great trouble in other words; "Attention!" is all right, but "Forward march!" is bad.

Our Major is a compact man; he has hardly a neck and is very energetic. They say he was a ribbon salesman before the war; he doesn't know much about soldiering except that he has enduring drive, and he thinks that to ride a horse well means to ride fast. I see him always galloping. He gives frequent pep speeches, and they have introduced a system of making men mad that is childish. Every candidate has to accompany the execution of a command with a grunt, ugh— "port arms, ugh" "at hease, ugh!" I think it does nothing to improve drilling.

This ribbon salesman Major has another wrong Idea. In the evening when we march the men back from the bayonet field, he sits on his horse, takes the salute, and as the companies pass, praises those who have the most broken bayonets. It is to him an indication of good work.

But bayonets are easily broken; I have shown my men how. When charging·the dummy, just press the butt to the side; the leverage will snap the bayonet right off in the center. I could march home without a single blade intact, but I don't carry it that far.

The Major is nice and when not in the saddle or on the drill grounds one can talk to him. I have observed how easy it is for men in the service here to acquire the spirit of the military. The young men from colleges absorb it quickly. There is a Captain here who is very young and out of Georgia Tech for a short while; he is every bit as arrogant as a German Lieutenant, bearing, voice, vanity, and all.

The Major addressed the Bayonet School; he said with his face purple: "When you see a German, you are looking at the worst so and so that God has created," and he spoke long and bitterly that way. Afterwards he turned to me and out of the side of his mouth said: "You know, I have to do this. This is a war."

He did another surprising thing. We have long latrines with many seats in a row, and there is in our barracks a young man who, because he has an uncle who is a Senator, manages to get leave to go to Atlanta when no one else can go or will, because there is so much to study. In consequence of this leave, he was behind in his work, and of course the Benzine Board would have flunked him even with the Senator uncle behind him; they do not fool. Well, this candidate went to the latrine and sat there with his drill regulations in one hand and the gun in the other, which he polished at the same time while studying in the book.

The Major passed by and shouted at him: "Hold it, hold it, stay there!" and then he ran out, and we who were outside had to come in. "Look at him, you guys," shouted the Major, "ten percent intelligence and ninety percent ambition is all you need in this man's army. Here's an example!" From then on he was the Major's pet.

In the evenings there are social functions of a very disappointing kind. The songs that are sung are below anything I have ever heard sung. One is so embarrassing that in the beginning the men only sang it with half voices; now they blare it out because they no longer think about the words. It goes:

I want the Bars, just like the Bars that my Lieutenant wears;
They are the Bars, the only Bars, and so on. . . .

It refers to getting a commission as a Second Lieutenant, who wears little gold bars on his shoulders.

We eat many chocolate bars, and at noon drink a colored liquid called Coca Cola. In the beginning I hated this drink, but it was the only thing at the stand and I was very thirsty from the sun and the exertion of bayonet drilling. Now it must be drunken, I long for it, and afterwards sit down in a very fine restful ease.

The food is good, the barracks crude but airy.

The landscape is not remarkable, but the climate is. In the morning when we march out, it is so cold that the men's fingers get numb, and at the halt some drop their guns because of this; at noon it is oppressively hot.

There are Negro labor battalions here, and I have much pleasure watching the colored men that are on guard. They creep along with bent knees as if held up by invisible strings, and they have found out how to carry their guns so that they float without effort over the shoulder. The gun lies on its side, the balance is worked out so that a little more weight is in back than in front and thus the butt holds up the hand. This hand is long, and the last joints of the fingers are pasted to the end of the gun. Their eyes are open but asleep; I am always afraid they will fall or walk into a tree; and the most wonderful performance is when they change the gun from one shoulder to the other. They hate to do this and go through the right motions but like in a dream. I am so fond of Negroes because I have never seen one until I came to America and they are therefore rare and interesting.

Since the latrine incident, they call the ribbon salesman Major "Ninety Percent." For some time now, I have observed on his side a feeling of suspicion towards me. At times he stands with other Officers; they speak together and then look at me. Most of them laugh and walk away. I am going to get mad about this laughing one day and tell them a few frank opinions.

The Senator's nephew has asked two of us to come along to a party. They say since the Army is here all the good families have left Atlanta, but a few without daughters have remained and we are to go to a house for a party.

We have not been drinking anything except this Coca Cola for a long time, no beer, no wine, but at this house are these drinks, also whisky. I drink a glass and it shakes me like a wet dog. But the other two are drinking it; they are more at home with this strong beverage. Spalding, who has been with me mostly on the bayonet field, is soon wobbly, and he says to me: "You're my pal."

But later on he comes again, and says: "You're my pal, but I'm not your pal! Oh, no—I'm not your pal!" and also: "You're going with me, but I'm not going with you."

And again, when I ask him why, he says: "You're my pal, but I'm not your pal!" and finally he takes his glass, and bangs it on the table, breaks it, and says: "Because you're a German spy."

The Senator's nephew, who can drink more, because he is always going out, told him to shut up.

We went home and I heard for the first time that there was a rumor that I was a spy, but that everybody laughed at that.

I was very angry and went to the Major and told him that, after all, the Germans weren't that stupid. He was sorry and everything seems allright again.

Today a Colonel from Headquarters sent for me; he invited me to sit down and spoke of many things, but nothing of the Army. He gave me a cigarette and then out of the blue sky asked me to tell him the Story of the Elephant Cutlet.

I had told this story only to Beardsley and the young priest. This officer knows Beardsley from the University, and how he heard of the story is very interesting.

Somebody in New York informed the police that I was a

German spy. The police, not knowing me, informed the Army;
the Army turned the information over to the Intelligence Department in Washington. Beardsley has been transferred to
that branch of the service in Paris. Checking up, the Army was
very thorough and among other things got in communication
with Beardsley. His correspondence came to Camp Gordon
with the rest. The Officer here wrote to Beardsley and Beardsley answered and wrote him to have me tell the Story of the
Elephant Cutlet. Again I love America, because it's wonderful
that in a great War like this, such nonsense can go on in
looking for a spy.

I told him the story, and since then have had to tell it to so
many people here that I am tired of it. It's about two men in
Vienna who wanted to open a restaurant.

THE ELEPHANT CUTLET

Once upon a time there were two men in Vienna who wanted
to open a restaurant. One was a Dentist who was tired of
fixing teeth and always wanted to own a restaurant, and the
the other a famous cook by the name of Souphans.

The Dentist was however a little afraid. "There are," he
says, "already too many restaurants in Vienna, restaurants of
every kind, Viennese, French, Italian, Chinese, American,
American-Chinese, Portuguese, Armenian, Dietary, Vegeta-
rian, Jewish, Wine and Beer Restaurants, in short all sorts of
restaurants."

But the Chef had an Idea. "There is one kind of restaurant
that Vienna has not," he said.

"What kind?" said the Dentist.

"A restaurant such as has never existed before, a restaurant for cutlets from every animal in the world."

The Dentist was afraid, but finally he agreed, and the famous Chef went out to buy a house, tables, and chairs, and engaged help, pots and pans and had a sign painted with big red letters ten feet high saying:

"Cutlets from Every Animal in the World."

The first customer that entered the door was a distinguished lady, a Countess. She sat down and asked for an Elephant Cutlet.

"How would Madame like this Elephant Cutlet cooked?" said the waiter.

"Oh, Milanaise, sauté in butter, with a little spaghetti over it, on that a filet of anchovy, and an olive on top," she said.

"That is very nice," said the waiter and went out to order it.

"Jessas Maria und Joseph!" said the Dentist when he heard the order, and he turned to the Chef and cried: "What did I tell you? Now what are we going to do?"

The Chef said nothing, he put on a clean apron and walked into the dining room to the table of the Lady. There he bowed, bent down to her and said: "Madame has ordered an Elephant Cutlet?"

"Yes," said the Countess.

"With spaghetti and a filet of anchovy and an olive?"

"Yes."

"Madame is all alone?"

"Yes, yes."

"Madame expects no one else?"

"No."

"And Madame wants only one cutlet?"

"Yes," said the Lady, "but why all these questions?"

"Because," said the Chef, "because, Madame, I am very sorry, but for one Cutlet we cannot cut up our Elephant."